Penguin Nature Guides

Rocks
and Pebbles

of Britain and Northern Europe

Troels V. Østergaard

Revised and adapted by John Whittow

Illustrated by Gregers Jensen
Translated from the Danish by David Matthews

Penguin Books

Penguin Books Ltd, Harmondsworth,
Middlesex, England
Penguin Books, 625 Madison Avenue,
New York, New York 10022, U.S.A.
Penguin Books Australia Ltd, Ringwood,
Victoria, Australia
Penguin Books Canada Ltd, 2801 John Street,
Markham, Ontario, Canada L 3 R 1 B 4
Penguin Books (N.Z.) Ltd, 182–190 Wairau Road,
Auckland 10, New Zealand

Sten og blokke first published by Gyldendal 1978
This translation published 1980

Printed in Portugal by Gris Impressores, Cacém
Filmset in Monophoto Times by Northumberland Press Ltd,
Gateshead, Tyne and Wear

549

Contents

Foreword

You have probably picked up a rock fragment many times – in the garden, on the beach or below a mountain crag – and wondered how it was formed and where it came from. Few of us are actually aware that there are hundreds of varieties of rock, or why they have such a multitude of colours and textures.

The term rock is often misused – usually we mean pebbles, which are the loose pieces of rock broken away from an outcrop (or exposure) of bedrock and which have sometimes moved a long distance from their original location, most frequently by running water, but occasionally by glaciers. Strictly speaking, a pebble's diameter is less than 64 mm; larger rock fragments are cobbles, boulders or blocks. The term stone is rarely used by professional geologists except to describe a particular type of rock, such as sandstone or limestone.

This basic handbook should help the beginner to discover and identify many types of pebbles and learn something about the way they were formed. Most of the selected examples are fairly commonplace, although a few are found only in northwestern Britain and Scandinavia.

Most of us are collectors by instinct – anyone strolling on the shingle beaches of northern Europe, scrambling in the rocky hills and mountains, or simply digging in the garden, may come across an unusual pebble and want to keep it as a souvenir or to start a collection. You do not have to be a specialist to enjoy these finds, and you do not need sophisticated and expensive equipment at this stage, although some people may decide to invest in a geological hammer and a magnifying glass as they progress towards more advanced learning and collecting.

We describe how certain deposits such as peat and diatomaceous earth are so soft that they cannot be regarded as being truly lithified (i.e. not true rocks) and thus will not form pebbles. They are included, however, to give the reader an idea of the range of deposits likely to be encountered. We also include some of the rare and special rocks and pebbles, found only in museums, so that the novice collector can build up a working knowledge of these as well as the common rock- and pebble-forming processes. We hope this will be an inspiration to move on to more advanced geological exploration.

Troels V. Østergaard

John Whittow

Unless indicated in the caption, all the illustrated pebbles are about three-quarters their natural size

Introduction

Most of us live in an urban world, far from the majestic rock outcrops of mountain and sea coast, and we do not realize that rocks are a part of the fabric of our towns and cities – as building stones, paving flagstones, street cobbles and roofing slates. Although artificial building materials are now widely used, many bricks and tiles are processed from natural clay rocks, our ubiquitous concrete is a mixture of pulverized limestone, often with an aggregate of fine pebbles (gravel), and our bitumen roads are generally composed largely of hard chippings of crushed igneous rocks. All this we take for granted, and it is only when we venture into the countryside that we begin to take more notice of the rocks and pebbles of our mineral world.

The shingle beaches we and our children enjoy so much, for example, are often a pebble collector's paradise, and in resorts like Brighton it is impossible not to be fascinated by the many different shapes and sizes to be found during a short stroll. In lesser-known localities, such as certain Cornish coves and Pembrokeshire bays, however, it is the wide variety of coloured pebbles which catch the eye. These different colours, shapes and textures clearly imply differences in composition and in the manner the rocks were formed. Even a child can begin to categorize his pebble collection into groups with similar colours or shapes without needing to know anything of rock-forming processes. But to a professional geologist, classification of rocks is a much more complicated business.

First of all, every specimen in the mineral world, exactly like every animal and plant, must have a name so that once it has been identified by its inherent characteristics it can always be recognized again. Unfortunately, it is not quite so simple when it comes to identifying pebbles. Two pebbles may be the same shape and colour but different of texture; or, other pebbles may be of identical colour and texture but different sizes and shapes. This difference, between plants and animals on the one hand and rocks and pebbles on the other, is due to one fundamental fact: the latter are inanimate, while plants and animals are alive. The appearance of a plant or animal depends on its internal genes and chromosomes but a pebble's is derived externally, from the nature of the original environment in which the rock-forming processes operated, as well as from the subsequent weathering and transportation of the pebble to its present resting place. We must learn something of these events before we can begin to identify and name our collection.

Although rocks seem to epitomize all that is permanent and solid in our environment, rock formation is, in fact, part of a dynamic endless process, where materials are created either at or beneath the earth's surface, are then compacted or solidified, uplifted and eroded, finally to be transported and re-deposited, or engulfed back into the bowels of the earth as part of the interminable cycle of lithogenesis (*lithos*: rock). There is a geological truism which refers to the formation of rocks: 'no vestige of a beginning – no prospect of an end'.

Pebble formation

We can start with mountains. These soaring, solid heights and crags, which seem so indestructible, are slowly but constantly worn down by the brutal force of the weather. Hence the term weathering, when the rock surface either crumbles, or splits and cracks, until large areas are loosened. The loosened material (regolith) sometimes remains to blanket the solid rock, but more frequently it moves away. Beneath a crag, loosened material falls by gravity or glissades down the slope. Alternatively, the regolith may be carried away by ice, water or wind to expose the fresh rock to the continuing action of weathering. This removal is termed erosion, and the ultimate character of the pebble will depend not only on its manner of transportation but also on the distance it has travelled.

Weathering

The two kinds of weathering are mechanical and chemical, and include several complex processes. The former is largely the result of frost action, which obviously requires sub-zero temperatures. In our era, therefore, such weathering takes place mainly in the Arctic and in high mountain regions. During the Ice Age, however, with its periods of colder climate, frost action was an important process over a considerable part of the northern hemisphere's land area. It must be remembered, therefore, that most of the pebbles now found in Britain were originally loosened by frost action which combines the alternate freezing and thawing of the intersticial moisture. In thaw conditions, the water seeps into the tiny cracks

Frost-riven limestone

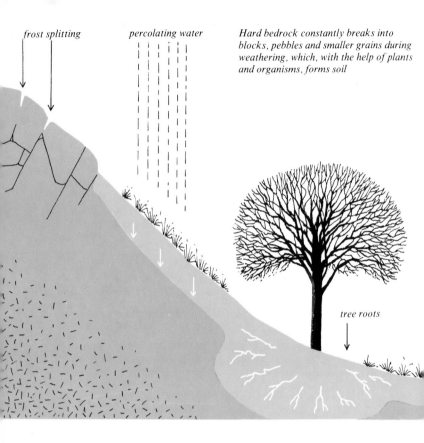

frost splitting

percolating water

Hard bedrock constantly breaks into blocks, pebbles and smaller grains during weathering, which, with the help of plants and organisms, forms soil

tree roots

which are always in the rock. Then, when the temperature falls below zero, the water freezes and expands, forcing the cracks to widen. The more frequent the change from freeze to thaw, the more rapid is the process of frost shattering.

The efficiency of mechanical weathering depends largely on how the rocks are jointed. Joints are formed by shrinkage as a result of cooling (in an igneous rock), by desiccation (in a sedimentary rock), or by the stresses associated with folding. Weathering is also governed by the grain size of igneous rocks and the particle size of sedimentary rocks. A coarse-grained granite, for example, weathers to a gravel which consists of individual mineral grains.

A gravel is composed of rock fragments of 2–4 mm in size and is therefore smaller than a pebble (4–64 mm). When rocks are fine-grained or have a small particle size, however, they are seamed with a joint network, usually picked out by weathering, to form cracks. Pieces of bedrock eventually split from the face to form almost rectangular blocks. If there is a more regular set of parallel cracks, as for example when the rock is a schist, flat fragments will be the result, and the same can happen if there are well-defined layers or bedding planes within a rock.

In mountain regions, where frost shattering is quite usual, the crash of loosened blocks can be heard as they fall down the mountain side, thawed by the power of the sun. The falling stones come to rest at the foot of the crag, in a so-called scree. Here the rock fragments are angular, retaining their corners and edges, for little has been knocked off as the loosened material toppled down. Furthermore, in winter there can often be a snowbank for the fragments to land on softly before they glissade downhill.

Mechanical weathering also includes the action of plant roots and the process of exfoliation (onion-skin weathering), when thin sheets of rock split off, due to extreme surface-temperature changes between night and day, mainly in the hot deserts, although periodic wetting speeds up the process.

Mechanical weathering is assisted in its rock-breaking activity by a group of actions collectively termed chemical weathering. In the case of frost action, this is especially concerned with percolating water since dry air by itself cannot carry out chemical weathering. Nevertheless, even a small moisture content is sufficient to generate chemical action. Rainwater takes up oxygen, carbon dioxide and other gases to form chemical solutions such as carbonic acid, i.e. carbon dioxide dissolved in water. In addition, other weak acids, including humic acid, from the decomposition of plant residues, contribute to chemical weathering in which the most important processes are reduction, oxidation, hydration and solution.

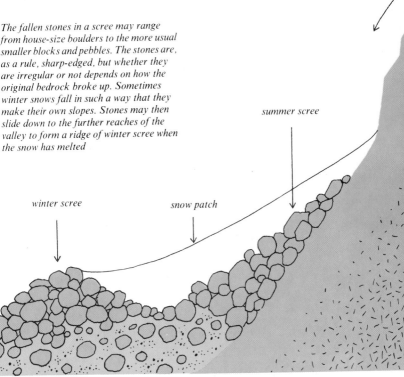

The fallen stones in a scree may range from house-size boulders to the more usual smaller blocks and pebbles. The stones are, as a rule, sharp-edged, but whether they are irregular or not depends on how the original bedrock broke up. Sometimes winter snows fall in such a way that they make their own slopes. Stones may then slide down to the further reaches of the valley to form a ridge of winter scree when the snow has melted

summer scree

winter scree

snow patch

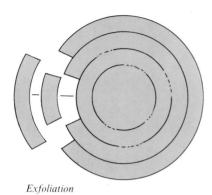

Exfoliation

The products of chemical weathering depend not only on the various combinations of these processes but also on the mineralogical make-up of the rocks themselves. Some minerals, such as quartz, are particularly resistant to chemical weathering, while others, such as the iron- and magnesium-rich silicates, are easily broken down into clay minerals. One of the most effective of these weathering processes is solution, especially in the case of the common sedimentary rock lime-stone (composed of calcium carbonate) which rapidly disintegrates when acted upon by rainfall or groundwater. The rock surfaces quickly become etched by the weathering and their joints enlarge to form fissures. These fretted surfaces create bare pavements, universally known as *karstic* landforms (of Yugoslavian derivation) but are locally termed *karrenfeld* (German) and *lapiés* (French). Because most limestone pebbles are relatively easily dissolved, they soon lose their angularity, especially when transported from the initial rock exposure. However, pebbles themselves often exhibit 'pitting' since the chemical solution process continues to operate, especially where there is plenty of percolating water to attack the weaker minerals.

In other instances the result of chemical weathering is illustrated by 'rotten' stones which are occasionally found, for example in gravel pits or in the soil. A 'rotten' stone crumbles in the fingers and often contains tiny gold flecks which are not real gold, only weathered mica.

'Rotten' stone

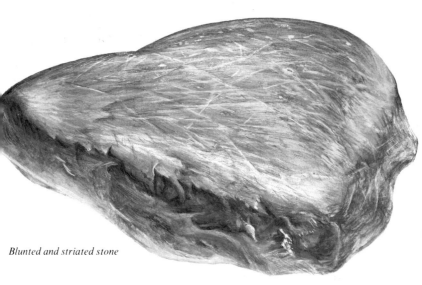

Blunted and striated stone

Ice-transported pebbles

A large proportion of the loose stony material in northern Europe and North America has been moved by ice. Even outside the areas where there were glaciers examples can be found that were affected by special climatic conditions during the Ice Age, such as wind-polished pebbles. Ice-transported pebbles have a characteristic blunted shape: sharp corners and edges have been knocked off but there has not been sufficient rounding to produce spherical or oval shapes. A unique type – the striated pebble – has scratches or glacial striae from grinding against other pebbles in the ice sheet or by being scraped along the underlying bedrock. The ice sheet's carrying ability is so powerful that enormous blocks can be moved far from their bedrock source. It was, in fact, the existence of such erratic blocks which originally convinced geologists that there actually was an Ice Age.

Some erratic blocks have been discovered at great distances from the known glacial limits, leading to the suggestion that they may have sailed even further while frozen into icebergs. Those derived from Scottish or Scandinavian ice sheets could travel south into the English

Ice cover (white area) during the last Ice Age

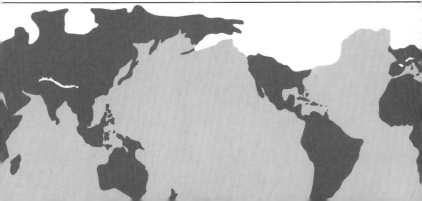

Channel, shedding boulders and pebbles en route as the ice melted. One such example is the 50-tonne seashore block at Porthleven in southern Cornwall. More commonly, however, ice-transported pebbles are found embedded in clay as a heterogeneous mass (boulder clay or till). The lack of sorting, as between boulders, cobbles and pebbles, distinguishes ice-deposited till from water-deposited materials which are well sorted. The composition and the orientation of the blocks within the glacial till are sometimes a clue to the direction in which former ice sheets moved.

Wind-eroded pebbles

A wide area outside the actual ice sheets lay bare or with only sparse vegetation during the Ice Age, and here the wind had free play to create sand and dust storms. Dust is found, for instance, in central Europe in the form of very fertile loess deposits, and wind-blown sand has scratched pebbles left behind by the ice. This sand-blasting effect can polish two, three or more facets on the exposed surfaces, forming the wind-polished stone or ventifact. Any pitting of the smoothness may represent etching of the weaker grains.

Wind-polished stone. The three large facets and the small one meet in characteristically sharp edges. The smaller drawing indicates how winds from different directions have developed the facets, by sand blasting

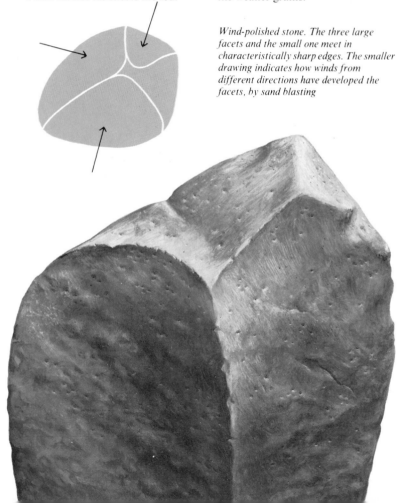

A pebble which has been worn almost spherical by rolling about in the water. The material does not show a tendency to split in a particular direction

Water-transported pebbles

Pebbles wear on all sides when carried by water, and thus become more or less rounded. This happens whether they are moved in rivers, ice-melt streams or by ocean waves. The rounded and completely smooth pebbles found on the seashore have rolled back and forth in the surf for thousands of years. This rough treatment removed sharp corners and edges and ground the pebble smooth, so that it eventually tended to become spherical if there was no previous 'inherited' shape, and if the material did not have an inbuilt tendency to erode more easily in one direction than another. Schists and slates, for example, have one marked splitting direction and tend to become flat discoidal pebbles. In rocks with two splitting directions the shapes formed depend on the way they split. If splitting was equally easy in either direction, a sausage shape may result, but if it was easier to split in one direction than in another, the conformation becomes more like a flat ellipse. When there are three splitting directions, a pebble can become almost spherical, as if it had no planes of weakness. With four splitting directions the shape may be flat, triangular or tetrahedral.

Two stones of a rock material without marked splitting directions. Although their initial shapes are different, both will wear away and become more and more rounded until they are almost spherical

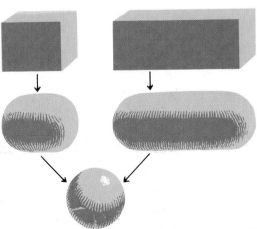

Rolled pebbles. Left: a flat elliptical shape from a rock with one marked splitting direction. Below: the four splitting directions will eventually make the stone flat and triangular

These shapes occur only if the pebbles are worn away for a long enough period of time, if the shape is primarily decided by the splitting directions and if the entire pebble is equally resistant. Otherwise, there is much individuality. One example is the waisted pebble, which consists of harder and softer layers. The soft layer wears away faster so that a furrow, or waist, develops. In other instances, calcareous shells can create points of weakness leading to the formation of hole-stones; more resistant material, such as groups of crystals or a quartz vein, can stand out in relief from an otherwise smoothly polished surface.

Ribbed stone. The grooves are made by the softer layers, which are less resistant to abrasion

Rock identification

Many people pick up unusually shaped or coloured pebbles, but how can they be identified? Rocks are divided into three main groups – sedimentary, metamorphic and igneous.

Sedimentary rocks are formed at the earth's surface by deposition (sedimentation) of material derived from the weathering and erosion of existing rocks. They also include material of organic and chemical origin, and three subdivisions have been recognized: the clastic sediments (sandstones, mudstones and conglomerates) built from fragments of pre-existing rocks; the organic sediments (some limestones, coal and some cherts); and the chemical sediments (gypsum and certain limestones, such as dolomite).

Metamorphic rocks are created when heat, pressure and hydrothermal processes act upon surrounding bedrock, thus causing mineralogical reactions together with textural and structural changes of the parent rock. There are four important types of metamorphism: thermal or contact, due to subterranean heat; dynamic, due to localized pressures, often at fault-lines; regional, when both heat and pressure create a wide range of new minerals and structures; and autometamorphism, when changes occur during the cooling of an igneous mass as a result of its residual fluids. The serpentine rocks of the Lizard, in Cornwall, were formed in this way.

Igneous or 'fire-formed' rocks are characteristically crystalline, but also include the glassy rock obsidian. Most igneous rocks have crystallized from a molten fluid (magma) in the earth's interior, and are generally composed of silicate minerals such as feldspars, pyroxenes and amphiboles. Igneous material may be extruded as the product of volcanic activity on the earth's surface or it may be intruded into the crustal rocks. Those rocks intruded at great depth, including most of the granites, are often referred to as plutonic. Thus, granite is only found at the surface after its cover of other rocks has been eroded. Igneous rocks are classified in several different ways – degree of acidity or basicity, colour, grain size or feldspar character.

To make rock identification easier, it is practical to make observations in sequence so that, for instance, you start with what can first be seen with the naked eye and then look at the more precise characteristics through a magnifying glass. The rock's colour, structure and grain or particle size are not difficult to see, but colour can sometimes be misleading since it can be made up of elements which are not always obvious. As an example, rocks which have been subject to oxidation during chemical weathering are usually rusty red on the outside, whatever their true colour. Furthermore, although most limestones are lighter coloured, there is a completely black variety, antrakonite.

The structure can also be layered – perhaps alternating light and dark, or with veins or folded layers. These features are helpful when making an identification as they are clues to the conditions under which the rock was formed.

Grain or particle size is critical in deciding how to continue. If the rock is so fine-grained that you cannot

How the grains of various minerals make up the composition of a rock

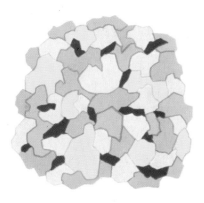

reddish minerals

whitish minerals

dark minerals

see a single grain, even with a magnifying glass, it is compact or structureless. In this case try to identify it with the help of the table on p.28. A coarser-grained rock – where the individual grains can be seen with or without a lens – contains two important clues for recognition: one is its mineral composition, the other is the interrelationship of the grains themselves, which may have 'grown together' in various ways.

Mineral identification

Rock-forming minerals must be distinguished from economic mineral deposits (e.g. ores). The strict definition of a rock-forming mineral is based on the premise that minerals are structurally homogeneous and are formed by the inorganic processes of nature. Nevertheless, most geologists treat organic limestones, siliceous rocks and phosphatic deposits as if their constituents were true mineral species.

Rocks can consist either of grains of a single mineral or of many different ones. Take granite, a fairly common rock, for example: it can be seen that its various grains are reddish, pale and dark. Closer observation reveals that not only the colour but also their shape and whole appearance separates them into three types. These are the minerals feldspar, quartz and biotite (dark mica). Several thousand different minerals have been identified, but all the common rocks consist mainly of only a score – the rock-forming minerals – in different combinations and proportions. Familiarity with ten of the most common ones will be a great help in identification.

Every mineral has a precise chemical composition and definite physical properties: crystal shape, colour, lustre, hardness, cleavage and density. To identify a mineral in a rock, look first for colour, hardness and cleavage. The investigation is easier if a knife, a piece of unglazed porcelain, a magnet and a small bottle of dilute hydrochloric acid (about a 10% solution) are at hand.

Minerals can be divided into two groups on the basis of their colour: light and dark. The pale rock-forming minerals are quartz, feldspar, muscovite and calcite, which may appear as clear, milky, greyish, pink or possibly pale green shades. The dark rock-forming minerals include pyroxene, amphibole, biotite, garnet and magnetite, which may be various shades of black, dark brown, green or red. The yellow metallic mineral pyrite cannot

21

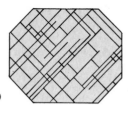

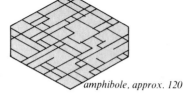

pyroxene, 90

amphibole, approx. 120

Above: angle of cleavage directions in pyroxene and amphibole.
Below: plagioclase with twinning stripes, best seen when turned in the light

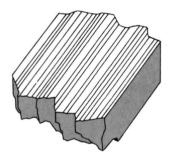

rock's constitution is, none the less, crystalline. This ordered crystal structure is indicated by, among other things, the cleavage which is characteristic for each mineral, such as feldspar, mica, pyroxene and amphibole. Cleavage occurs when a mineral's crystal structure is relatively weak in certain directions, along which it can be easily split into pieces (cleavage directions). The cleavage surfaces can usually be recognized by their comparatively regular arrangement, and they also tend to be shinier than ordinary fracture surfaces.

When a mineral has more than one cleavage direction, the angle between them is important for identification. In the case of pyroxene and amphibole, which look very much alike, each has two cleavage directions. In pyroxene the angle between them is 90 , but in amphibole it is 120 .

readily be placed in either group, but it is easily recognized.

Hardness is tested by scratching. Some minerals, such as mica, are so soft that they can be scratched with a fingernail, while others, such as calcite, require a knife to make a mark. Feldspar is even harder to scratch with a knife, and quartz cannot be scratched at all – it is so hard that it will even scratch glass.

All minerals are crystalline material – their atoms are arranged in a precisely determined pattern, and their crystal structure reveals itself externally in the form of beautiful crystals. Well-shaped crystals are rarely found in common rocks, except in the case of garnet, but a

Certain minerals are actually families. Feldspar is, in fact, a collective noun for many minerals of which the most important are alkalifeldspar and plagioclase. Plagioclase can often be recognized by a fine striping – like a closed book seen from the side – more easily seen when turned in the light. Alkalifeldspar is not striped. Similarly, pyroxene and amphibole are mineral family names. The descriptions on the next pages summarize the characteristics of ten common minerals when they form part of a common rock.

QUARTZ

Colour: usually white to colourless
Hardness: very hard; irregular fracture
Cleavage: none; irregular fracture
Identification: hardness and colour may resemble glass
Occurrence: spread over all rock groups, in sandstone and granite, and as veins

FELDSPAR

Colour: reddish, pink or greyish
Hardness: difficult to scratch
Cleavage: two cleavage directions at right angles to each other
Identification: colour, cleavage, glassy lustre
Occurrence: common in all rock groups: sandstone, granite, pegmatite and gneiss

MUSCOVITE (pale mica)

Colour: pale, yellowish, semi-transparent
Hardness: can be scratched with a fingernail
Cleavage: one main direction
Identification: colour; can be peeled into flakes with fingernail
Occurrence: in pale granite, pegmatite, mica schist and gneiss

CALCITE

Colour: most often white
Hardness: can be scratched with a knife
Cleavage: rhombohedral (six equal planes with rhombic angles)
Identification: hardness and colour; bubbles with cold 10% hydrochloric acid
Occurrence: chalk, limestone and marble

PYRITE ('fool's gold')

Colour: brassy yellow, metallic lustre
Hardness: can be scratched with a knife
Cleavage: not noticeable
Identification: colour and lustre; often found as typically cube-shaped crystals
Occurrence: common in black schists; forms concretions and occurs as an ore of iron

AMPHIBOLE

Colour: opaque black or brownish
Hardness: cannot be scratched with a knife
Cleavage: two directions at an angle of about 120 to each other
Identification: colour and cleavage
Occurrence: especially common in metamorphic rocks such as amphibolite and gneiss

PYROXENE

Colour: opaque black or brownish
Hardness: cannot be scratched with a knife
Cleavage: two directions at 90 angles to each other
Identification: colour and cleavage
Occurrence: common in igneous rocks such as basalt, gabbro and peridotite

BIOTITE (dark mica)

Colour: brown-black to black
Hardness: can be scratched with a fingernail
Cleavage: one prominent direction
Identification: colour; can be peeled into flakes with a fingernail
Occurrence: common in granite, syenite, porphyries, mica schist and gneiss

GARNET

Colour: usually brown-red to deep red
Hardness: cannot be scratched with a knife
Cleavage: none; irregular or conchoidal fracture
Identification: forms beautiful crystals with a characteristic shape and appearance
Occurrence: particularly in metamorphic rocks such as mica schist

MAGNETITE (*below*)

Colour: black with a metallic lustre
Hardness: can barely be scratched with a knife
Cleavage: none
Identification: the only mineral attracted by a pocket magnet
Occurrence: minor but common constituent of many rocks; found as iron ore and in common beach sands

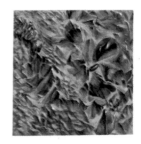

Rock 'textures'

Texture is the relationship between the mineral grains that form a rock. Sedimentary rock textures are related to the grain properties of size, sorting, shape, arrangement, porosity and permeability. The rock fabric and the type of process which produced the sediment can be determined from these characteristics. Metamorphic rock textures are governed largely by grain size, but the minerals of the finest-grained rocks (e.g. slates) are almost indistinguishable. Prolonged metamorphism produces coarse textures with large mineral grains. Autometamorphism produces very coarse-grained rocks, such as marbles. The texture of igneous rocks is broadly related to their rate of cooling and consolidation. In general, fine-grained and glassy rocks are due to rapid cooling and coarse-grained ones to slow cooling deep in the earth. The illustrations below and at the top of p. 26 show a cut and polished sample of similar sedimentary rocks and the texture which emerges as the particle boundaries are distinguished. It is clear that although the particle sizes are different, the textures are broadly similar. They consist of more or less rounded granules, packed tightly together. Both are conglomerates; the first is a polymict variety of large and small pebbles of a mixture of rocks, and the second is an oligomict variety, formed mainly from quartzite pebbles and with one dominant particle size.

Pebble texture in a conglomerate

Pebble texture in a quartzite conglomerate

Augen gneiss and amphibolite are examples of metamorphic rocks. Their textures are not very similar but they both have elongated grains with more or less parallel orientation. In the one case all the elongated grains are parallel, while in the other, stripes are draped around the larger grains, but within each stripe the grains are parallel. Certainly a rock consisting solely of parallel elongated grains has a strong tendency to split along the length of the grains. This type of rock is schistose,

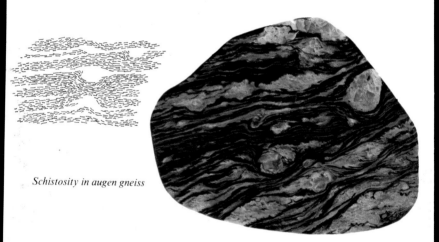

Schistosity in augen gneiss

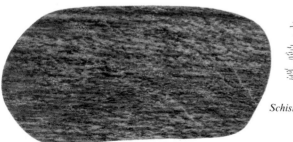

Schistosity in amphibolite

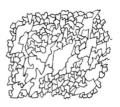

*Graphic texture in granite
with fine-grained groundmass*

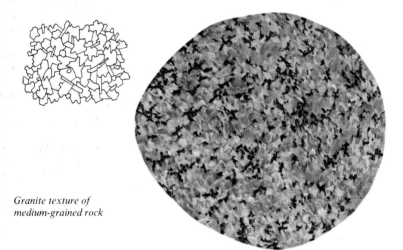

*Granite texture of
medium-grained rock*

and the texture formed through the parallel orientation of mineral grains is schistosity, even though the rock itself may not be called a schist. Schistosity is a characteristic of many metamorphic rocks.

The third major group, the igneous rock textures, is exemplified by the accompanying illustrations. Igneous grain sizes are always determined on the general groundmass, so that large crystals (phenocrysts) are ignored. The drawings show how grains have grown by simultaneous crystallization of minerals, to look like a jigsaw. The upper example has a graphic texture similar to cuneiform lettering; the lower granite, with a coarser groundmass texture, is a medium-grained rock with a uniform 'granitic' texture. These igneous rocks, characterized by large crystals (phenocrysts) enclosed in a finer-grained groundmass, are called porphyries. In many instances this porphyry texture is very distinctive.

27

These textures are only a few of the many which characterize our rocks, but all are the result of formative processes which differ considerably not only between the three main rock groups (sedimentary, metamorphic and igneous) but also within each individual group. In the following pages there is a discussion as to why sedimentary rock textures differ not only from each other (e.g. sandstone from chalk) because of their different modes of formation, but also how they differ considerably from the metamorphic rock textures and from the fire-formed igneous rocks.

Recognizing fine-grained rocks

It may be difficult to identify a very fine-grained rock – one in which the grains cannot be seen without a lens. Look for layering, which points to a sedimentary origin, or for flow lines which can mean a volcanic origin. The colour may be of some help and you can also decide if it is calcareous by testing with acid. A sedimentary rock can be recognized by its fossil content or the imprints of other organisms. Hardness alone, unlike that of a mineral, is no real guide, because in a rock this depends mainly on how well the grains stick together. In addition, a number of rocks, such as limestone and mudstone, can be silicified and are therefore harder.

The table below lists a few characteristics of rocks described in the text and may help you to start identifying your finds.

Structureless rocks

colour: black or dark

hard rock with conchoidal fracture	flint	p. 49
glassy lustre and conchoidal fracture	obsidian	p. 108
hard rock with or without cavities	compact basalt	p. 101

colour: pale

hard, vesicular rock	pumice	p. 107
soft, bubbles when treated with acid	limestone	p. 42
rust-coloured	ironstone	p. 55

Rocks with structure

rock shows bedding	siltstone, mudstone	p. 36, 39
rock shows flow texture	andesite	p. 104

Schistose rocks — schists — p. 72

Sedimentary rocks

A sediment is a rock formed on, or very close to, the earth's surface as a result of 'surface' action such as weathering, transport and deposition. Most sediments are loose and unconsolidated when they are deposited, but become transformed by compaction and various chemical reactions (diagenesis) into solid rocks. The appearance of a fully-formed sedimentary rock is thus decided by: the nature of the original rock that was weathered; the conditions during weathering, transport and deposition, and diagenesis after deposition.

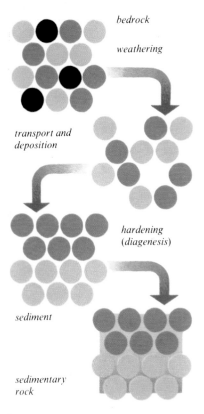

bedrock

weathering

transport and deposition

hardening (diagenesis)

sediment

sedimentary rock

It may be said that these processes tend to level out the earth's surface: they displace material from higher areas and carry them along until finally they reach the sea. On its way, the sedimentary material may stay for a short or longer period in the alluvial plains where both deposition and erosion take place. However, the two processes are more or less balanced so that the shape of the alluvial plain alters only slowly. In the sea, sedimentation is the dominant process.

Depositional environments

A mountain foot (piedmont) is the area between mountains and lowland. The sediments deposited there are, as a rule, coarse and poorly sorted. On the highest slopes, the fallen material is mainly scree. Lower down, the material may be washed down by running water or slide down as mudflows.

Alluvial plain sediments are finer-grained and better sorted than those of the piedmont zone. Where the alluvial plain abuts against the piedmont, the slope is fairly steep, the streams form a 'network' and the sediments are quite coarse. Lower down, as the slope eases, the water concentrates into meandering rivers which carry fine-grained sediments. As the meanders change course they cause both erosion and deposition in the river channel, for at a river bend the water's speed is greatest on the outside of the curve, which erodes the bank. Conversely, speed is lowest on the inside bend (the slip-off slope) and so material is deposited there. In this way, the river constantly moves its bed backwards and forwards over the alluvial plain, continually eroding and re-sorting the

29

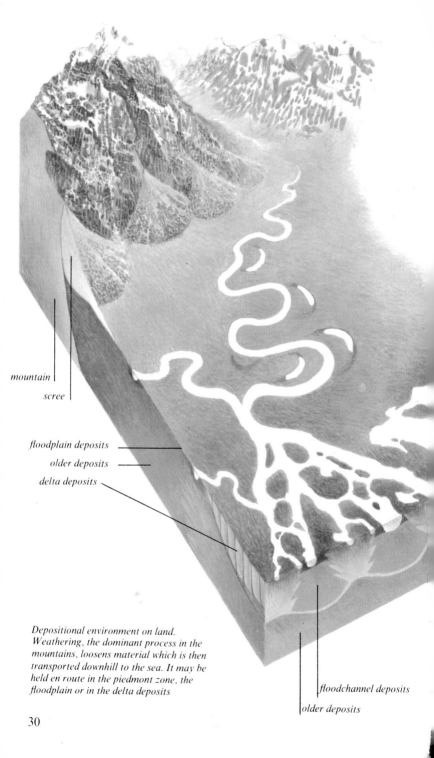

mountain

scree

floodplain deposits

older deposits

delta deposits

*Depositional environment on land.
Weathering, the dominant process in the
mountains, loosens material which is then
transported downhill to the sea. It may be
held en route in the piedmont zone, the
floodplain or in the delta deposits*

floodchannel deposits

older deposits

deposits. Time and again a part of the river channel becomes cut off and forms an oxbow lake where fine muds are deposited.

On the alluvial plain itself, material is laid down whenever the river bursts its banks. Since most of this is deposited close to the river, a natural bank (levée) builds up along the channel edges. Further out on the floodplain every flood leaves a thin layer of mud.

A delta forms where a river runs out into fairly still water, such as a lake or the sea. The transported material is left behind as the current slows down, the coarser near the shore and the finer further out. If there is a constant supply, the deposits eventually build up above the surface and form a new alluvial plain. Seawards from the shore, material continues to be deposited on a very gradual slope, again with

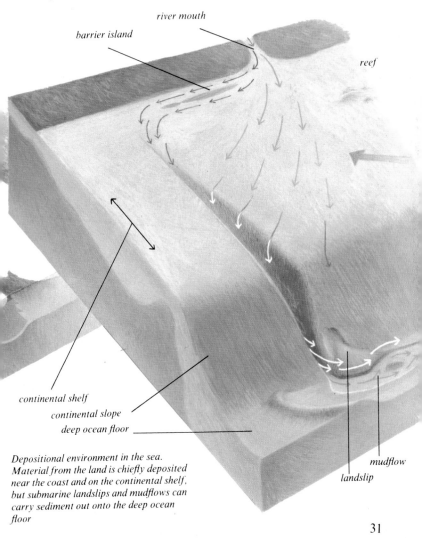

river mouth

barrier island

reef

continental shelf
continental slope
deep ocean floor

mudflow

landslip

Depositional environment in the sea. Material from the land is chiefly deposited near the coast and on the continental shelf, but submarine landslips and mudflows can carry sediment out onto the deep ocean floor

31

the coarsest nearest the shore. As a delta gradually builds up over its own deposits, the deltaic sediments are always finest at the bottom and become coarser towards the top.

On barrier coasts, where wave action is stronger, deltas cannot form. The material carried by the rivers is sorted by the wave movements so that the coarser sand is moved onto and partly along the shore, but the finer-grained is carried away. The sand forms sandbanks which sometimes develop into barrier islands.

The continental shelf is the zone of shallow water between the coast and the continental slope, where the ocean suddenly deepens. Material set down on this very gently sloping surface is mainly derived from land, and is carried out by currents. The finest clay is deposited furthest out, where the water is so deep that wave action does not affect the bottom. Sandbanks and bars are formed nearer to land and sometimes – if conditions are right – calcareous banks such as coral reefs. The continental shelf is cut through by deep valleys called submarine canyons. They open out at the continental slope foot into the ocean's deep abyssal zone. The distance to shore is now so great that one should not really expect to find material originating there, but as nearshore deposits become unstable they flow out from the continental margin to cover the deep ocean floor as submarine mudflows. Coarser material is transported out through the submarine canyons at the same time.

A characteristic mixture of sediments is deposited in each of these kinds of environment: in an alluvial plain, for example, the coarsest sediment remains in the river channel itself, and the finest in oxbow lakes and levées. The floodplain is gradually built up by such materials,

but as the river changes course new oxbow lakes and levées are created. Initially there is an orderly relationship between the various kinds of sediment. Levée sediments, for instance, are found adjacent to channel sediments, but both may ultimately be cut through and partially destroyed by a migrating river channel with its new sedimentary sequence. River channel sediments, lake sediments and deltaic sediments, each with their own distinctive character-

Section through a sequence of deposits. The sediments follow each other in succession, depending on the changes in the depositional environment

Delta sediments

Marine sediments. The swamp is completely flooded

Coal seams. As the water level rises, the forest becomes a swamp in which plant material accumulates

Sandy sediments with remains of tree stumps

istics, can therefore replace each other, and their interrelationships play an important part in any attempted reconstruction of the former sedimentary environments.

Where a piece of sedimentary rock has been detached from its surroundings it is difficult to determine the environment from which it came. Two sandstones may appear to be exactly the same, with the same particle size, but one could have come from a river deposit and the other from the sea. When two sediments have the same particle size, it is probable that they were formed by currents with about the same speed. In many cases, however, instead of using the term 'currents' or 'movement back and forth' (e.g. by waves), one refers to the energy content of the sediment rather than the current speed. Coarse sediments are deposited in a high-energy environment, and finer-grained sediments in a low-energy one.

Fine-grained, cross-bedded sandstone with scattered shell fragments. Cross-bedding indicates that it has been deposited in flowing water, but the fine grain size shows that the current was weak. The pattern (lower right) is a disturbance in the layers which may have been caused by a methane (marsh gas) bubble

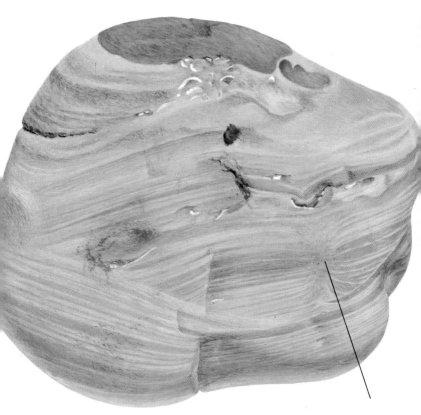

Transported sediments

The different sedimentary environments are not all equally represented in a random collection of pebbles. Erosion is the dominant process in high mountain areas and it is thus rather rare that piedmont-zone deposits 'survive' long enough to consolidate into the rocks from which pebbles form. On the other hand, sediments in the sea or on low-lying land will probably escape erosion until they become hard rocks. Areas where deposition has been the dominant process throughout a long period of time are called basins.

Sediments formed of material from outside a depositional basin are treated as a separate group – transported (mechanical) sediments – in the following pages. These rocks are divided by particle size into conglomerate, sandstone, siltstone and mudstone, together with clay and shale.

Conglomerates

Conglomerates are coarse rocks with an obvious pebble texture. The more or less rounded individual particles are over 2 mm in diameter and are composed of former rocks. There are pebbles of the same rock type in some kinds of conglomerates, but in others they are mixed. There may be varying amounts of fine-grained matrix between the pebbles.

In a quartzite conglomerate all the pebbles are quartzite. Clay gall conglomerate is made up of mudstone fragments (clay galls) embedded in a muddy rock. Thus both fragments and matrix are of the same material. In tillite (lithified till) the pebbles are often of different rocks, are not very rounded, may have glacial striae, and a large proportion of the matrix may be rock fragments.

A conglomerate-like rock with sharp-edged fragments is breccia. This can be consolidated scree but

Quartzite conglomerate with rounded, fine-grained quartzite pebbles in a coarse quartzitic matrix. The rock's constituents are more easily identified on the surfaces which have been exposed to weathering

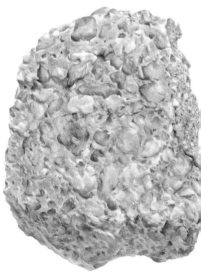

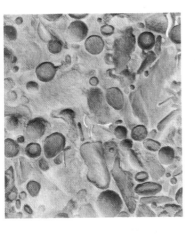

Clay gall conglomerate with rounded, iron-bearing mudstone fragments in a grey, fine-grained matrix. Pebbles have fallen out of the pits on the surface. The furrows around many pebbles indicate that the surrounding material is soft

more often is broken and crushed rock with later in-filling of the fractures. Agglomerate resembles conglomerate, but is made of volcanic (igneous) material.

Conglomerates with a small degree of matrix are usually formed by cemented pebble deposits near coasts, while clay gall conglomerates are the result of tidal action. When large areas dry out at low tide their bottom sediments crack up into dry, partly loose flakes. When the tide comes in the flakes break free and slide around, to be deposited with the next layer of bottom mud ('silt'). Those conglomerates with a quantity of matrix between the grains come

from material of various kinds deposited in landslides, or from solidified glacial till (tillite) created by compaction of very ancient moraines.

Conglomerates are not very widespread in occurrence but one important type is certainly the basal conglomerate which often underlies a series of marine deposits. It marks the tidal zone in coastal areas where the sea has inundated the land – a transgression. While the area is submerged, various marine sediments may be deposited and, in certain cases, another conglomerate can occur above them as the sea retreats – a regression.

basal conglomerate ⎯⎯⎯

older layers ⎯⎯⎯

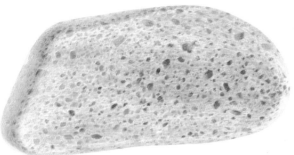

Orthoquartzite rock is pale and coarse-grained. In the diagram below notice how the fracture follows grain boundaries on the orthoquartzite's broken surface

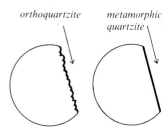

orthoquartzite   metamorphic quartzite

Sandstone and siltstone

The grains of sandstone and siltstone are rounded. The particle size in sandstone is between 2–0.06 mm, and in siltstone 0.06–0.004 mm. The smallest particles are only barely visible under a lens. Their quartz grains make most sandstones and many siltstones a light colour. A reddish hue is the result of the feldspar content or an iron oxide ('rust') stain in the grains. Sometimes these sediments are darkened by the minerals in them, or because there is a dark matrix between the sand grains. There may also be various other kinds of sedimentary structures such as bedding and crossbedding.

Sedimentary rock which consists almost entirely of quartz is called orthoquartzite, and should not be confused with a metamorphic quartzite. To distinguish one from the other, break off a corner: if the surface follows the grain boundaries it is an orthoquartzite, and if it cuts across the grains it is a meta-quartzite (see p. 64). Both are whitish, greyish or reddish. The greenish mineral glauconite, often found in sandstones, gives the colour to greensand in its unweathered state. Iron oxides stain most sandstones red or brown, but there are some spotted varieties. Sandstone which, in addition to quartz grains, contains more than

Greensand. A magnifying glass would help to locate the pale quartz and dark green grains of the mineral glauconite in a freshly broken rock

36

25% feldspar, is arkose. It is this feldspar content which often gives it a red hue. Sand grains are predominant in each of these sandstone types but in some examples when a cementing matrix is more than 15% of the volume, the rock is a greywacke. A greywacke, usually dark grey, can contain, in addition to quartz and feldspar, small blunt particles such as bits of schist.

It has been noted how quartzitic rocks can also be formed through metamorphism. When the sandstone particle is angular instead of rounded the rock is a grit. Deposits of consolidated volcanic ash, called tuff, sometimes show current-bedding if they are water-lain, and it can be very difficult to tell the difference between a real tuff and a sandstone composed of weathered material from a volcanic area.

Above right: cross-bedded arkose with pale and reddish layers. The red colour comes from the feldspar and coatings of the iron mineral haematite

Right: spotted sandstone. A haematite coating around each sand grain makes the pebble red. The colourless spots are probably haematite converted to soluble iron compounds by the remains of organic material

Greywacke can be identified by its various grey shades and the relatively large amount of fine-grained matrix between the sand grains

The appearance of sandstone, found in many different depositional environments, depends on the source rock and the manner of formation. A granitic rock, comprising the minerals quartz, feldspar and mica, will, for example, weather to a feldspathic sand which hardens to form an arkose. Sandstones seldom contain mica, since its flakes easily float in the water and are not deposited with the sand grains.

Feldspar grains are not particularly resistant to abrasion and in contrast to quartz grains stand up poorly to transport. Therefore, the feldspar content of a sandstone is a measure of how far the material has been transported. Arkoses are, in this respect, immature polymict rocks composed of sand which has been carried for only a relatively short time. At the other end of the scale we have the mature, pure, oligomict orthoquartzite which is probably created during several cycles – eroding of a feldspathic sandstone, followed by renewed movement and then deposition of the purer sediment.

Greywacke, like arkose, is an immature rock. It is usually formed by the hardening of mudflows from the continental slope foot, but it can also be made up of weathered material from volcanic rocks.

The shell fragments in siltstone clearly point to a sedimentary origin. A lens will magnify the rounded grain texture in this pale, fine-grained rock

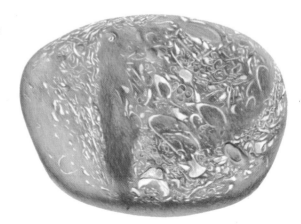

The shape of individual sand grains and their degree of sorting tell us a great deal about how a sediment was formed. A sandstone is said to be well sorted if all the grains are similar, and poorly sorted if there are many different sizes. For instance, sandstone from desert sand is often well sorted, with rounded grains. Sandstone deposits are an important clue when building up a picture of ancient geological and geographical environments and of how the deposits were formed. A sandstone's mineral content can reveal the rock type from which the material was derived, and thus indicate the geological pattern of the eroded area. Geographical conditions such as water depth, current strength and transport direction can be deduced from the cross-bedding and 'ripple marks'.

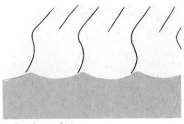

'Ripple marks'

colour, while carbonaceous material results in darker shades. Many mudstones and shales are so soft that they can be cut with a knife, but with silicification they become hard rocks that cannot be scratched. Both types can show bedding, with layers of different colours or of slightly different grain sizes. Shale can also be recognized by its fissility, the ease with which it splits along planes parallel to the original bedding.

Mudstone and shale

Mudstone and shale are so fine-grained that the individual grains cannot be seen without a lens. Their three main constituents, which can occur in different proportions, are clay, calcium carbonate (lime) and carbonaceous material. The presence of lime gives a lighter

Silicified mudstone is so compact that its texture cannot easily be seen. The structures – bedding disturbed by slumping (above) and bedding and cross-bedding (below) – at least indicate that it is sedimentary in origin

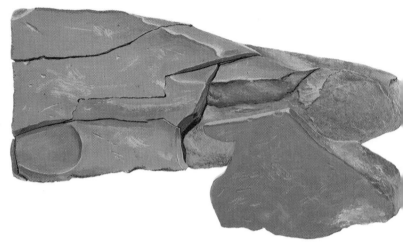

Shale is a very fine-grained greenish rock with weak bedding. Its fissility is parallel to the bedding direction

Clay is a fine-grained sedimentary rock without fissility, often containing some organic material. If the rock is predominantly mud it is mudstone; if it contains mud and lime it is marl (cementstone). Lime content can be verified with the help of the acid test.

Shale can be confused with metamorphic slate. A shale with a large carbonaceous content, usually black, is bituminous shale. This type is common in Jurassic rocks in England, for instance at Kimmeridge, Dorset. There is such a high organic content in oil-shale that oil can be extracted from it.

Very fine-grained rocks imply such still water that the fine particles sink to the bottom. This occurs in lakes and lagoons near the coast, or in deep water where there are no waves or currents. Newly-deposited sediments may be up to 80% water.

Thus there is a pronounced settling as a new sediment loses its water and develops into a solid rock. The waterlogged sediment is, in a sense, fluid and can be set in motion by earth tremors, for example, to slide down quite gentle slopes. The different layers then become mixed, creating a feature in solid rocks known as slump structures.

Black bituminous shale forms naturally, but only where carbonaceous material has not decomposed. The deposited organic matter is usually dead plankton, which sinks to the bottom. If the water is oxygenated, bacteria then break down the organic matter, but this uses up the oxygen; if new oxygen is not available the process soon stops. This is especially true in lakes and land-locked seas, such as the Black Sea and other seas with limited water circulation.

Mudstone and shale are formed in many depositional environments on land and in the sea. It is normally possible to tell from the fossil content whether a deposit is from fresh or salt water, and in fine-grained sediments there is always a good chance of finding well-preserved fossils. Mudstones and shales with high carbonaceous content are created under more special conditions and are particularly important because their carbonaceous matter can, in many cases, develop into oil and gas.

Non-transported sediments

The second main group of sedimentary rocks is called non-transported, since the material forming the rock comes from the depositional basin itself. Non-transported sediments consist mainly of dead plant and animal remains. One type is the many kinds of chalk, peat, coal and similar rocks (biogenic sediments) created by biological processes. Another is chemical, chiefly from chemical precipitates, such as rock salt, made by the evaporation of sea water. These rocks are rarely found as pebbles. Siliceous rock and iron-rich sediments are reckoned as chemical sediments, but it should be emphasized that there is no sharp division between the biogenic and the chemical sediments, since each process can also be involved in the other. This is why the types are grouped under the general heading of non-transported sediments.

Transported sediments

Non-transported sediments

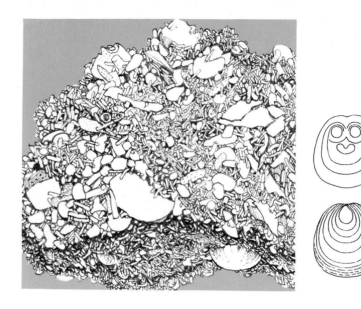

Limestone and dolomite

The most important diagnostic feature of limestone is its reaction to the acid test, since nearly all limestone is calcite in one form or another. As a rule, limestone is light coloured, but different impurities can cause deeper shades – yellowish, greenish, red, or even black. One type is composed of shells, broken bits of coral stems or other calciferous material from animals or plants, all cemented together. Another kind is compact, with only a few plant and animal remains, while a third is of calcite crystals with a jigsaw-puzzle texture.

Dolomite resembles limestone in many respects, except that its most important mineral is not calcite but the double carbonate of calcium and magnesium. The two minerals are similar, but dolomite does not bubble with cold hydrochloric acid; the acid must first be warmed.

Many limestones are mainly of shells or other obvious biological products and take their name from the dominant one: coral limestone is chiefly made up of partly disintegrated coral stems. In some types the space between the coral fragments is filled with fine-grained calcareous mud that makes the rock compact. In other instances you may find a porous rock of hardened chalk mud from which the coral fragments have been dissolved, leaving only their impressions. A coarse-grained calcareous specimen of different kinds of shells or bits of shells, especially mussels, brachiopods (lamp shells), sea-urchins, sea-urchin spines or coral stems, is shelly limestone. Limestone dominated by crinoid fragments is crinoidal limestone, while the remains of Bryozoa (aquatic organisms) is bryozoan limestone. A number of limestones are made from the shells of the single-celled organism Foraminifera which

Left: shelly limestone consists of shells, shell fragments and chalk particles washed together. Detail: some of the shells are from the brachiopod Crania

Right: a rare and unusual coral limestone from Faxe, Denmark. The broken pieces of coral stems lie partly 'free', without chalk in the interstices. The covering is more like a chalky mudstone

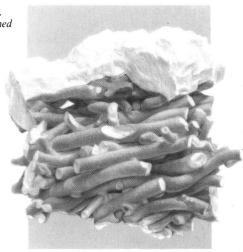

is so small that it can only be seen under a microscope. There are exceptions, however: numulite shells, for example, which are the chief constituents of numulitic limestone, are about the size and shape of a one-penny piece. The genus Fusilina (spindle-shaped, 2–3 mm long) and Schwagerina (spherical, 1–2 mm) predominate in fusilina and schwagerina limestones respectively.

Below left: broken pieces of sea-lily (crinoid) are common in many limestones. If they are the main constituent, the rock is crinoidal limestone

Below right: numulites belong to the group Foraminifera which includes large calcareous shells. Numulitic limestone, consisting mainly of these shells, was used in the construction of the Egyptian pyramids

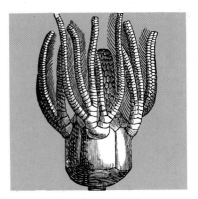

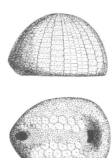

Different kinds of sea-urchin spines are often fossilized in chalk, a soft, white, crumbly, compact calcareous rock. It may also contain concretions of flint or pyrite (p. 58)

Oolitic limestone is built up of many small calcareous spheres – the so-called ooliths (like fish roe). The drawing is twice life-size

Compact calcareous rocks without any special structure are calcareous mudstones, of which one variety is chalk, a soft white limestone. Chalk often contains shell fossils, sea-urchin spines and similar material, and impressions of sea-urchins replaced by flint. Travertine is usually layered, fine-grained or compact, often porous, and identified by the impressions of leaves and stems of land plants. Crusty algal limestone, also in the compact group, developed from algae which covered the ocean floor.

There is a limestone group that is not compact – the visible grains are of chemical, not biological, origin. Oolitic and pisolitic limestones are calcareous pellets which, when they are small, are called ooliths and, when larger, pisoliths. Antrakonite is coarsely crystalline and can be black. Its other name is stinkstone, from its unpleasant sulphurous smell when broken. Marble is a rather coarsely crystalline limestone which has been metamorphosed. It bubbles like other limestones when tested with acid, but because of its transformation there are no traces of shells or other fossils.

It has been seen how limestone comes from material deposited by living organisms or by chemical precipitation. Shelly and crinoidal limestones, for example, are clearly produced by the first method. Nevertheless, it is not so obvious that chalk is made up by the deposition of shells. Examination under a powerful microscope reveals that it consists almost entirely of tiny oval calcareous plates, coccoliths, which were once the shells of single-celled organisms.

Calcareous mud may originate from chemical precipitation, but more often consists of shelly material ground off by surf and water currents. Oolitic and pisolitic limestones develop on the ocean floor purely by chemical processes in areas with calcareous mud precipitation – a present-day example is the Great Bahama Bank. The constant water movement keeps the small spheres in motion so that deposition takes place all around them.

Travertine also results from a purely chemical process, where lime-rich groundwater flows onto the surface. Lime (calcium carbonate) is only slightly soluble in pure water, but its solubility increases if a component of the water is carbon dioxide (carbonic acid). Groundwater that has become carbon dioxide-rich by seeping through the earth can dissolve some of the underlying limestone and so become 'hard'. When this 'hard' ground-

Travertine (tufa).
Note the
characteristic imprint
of stems and leaves

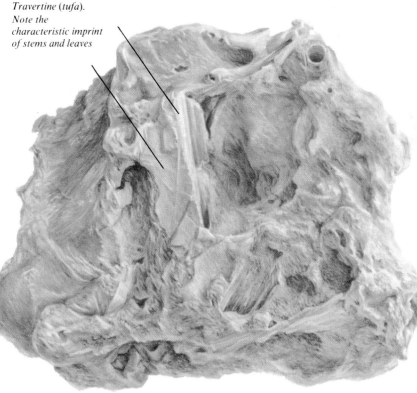

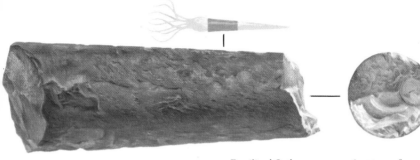

Fossilized Orthocerus, an extinct type of cephalopod, is a feature in red limestone from Øland, Sweden. It can also be found in other limestones from the Silurian period

water returns to the surface, for example in springs, it must release carbon dioxide into the atmosphere, and it therefore deposits lime as travertine.

Antrakonite is composed of flat balls (concretions) of lime in layers of other sedimentary rocks, often shales. Exactly how this formation takes place is not known, but perhaps it is after deposition and before hardening. Following deposition, limestone is subjected to diagenesis which more or less obliterates the original structure, making it impossible to tell how the stone was formed. Coral and other porous limestones develop into compact rocks if the pores are filled with calcareous mud. In other cases lime may be redistributed by solution and redeposition. For example, the lime in dissolved coral twigs can re-form in pores and holes in other parts of the rock. You may find sea-urchin shells that have become filled in this way with beautiful calcite crystals or crystal groups.

Part of the later development of limestone results from calcium carbonate forming two different minerals, calcite and aragonite. The latter comes from lime precipitated out as 'scale'. Aragonite is found naturally in some mussels and other shells but it changes with time into calcite so that many of the finer details in the shell disappear. The rock dolomite is created from limestone by a chemical reaction which converts an original calcium carbonate into a calcium magnesium carbonate. In this way the mineral calcite changes to the mineral dolomite, but it is not known how this actually takes place; it may be that newly-deposited limestone reacts with sea water, and at a later stage there is a reaction between the limestone and percolating solutions.

Antrakonite concretion in shale

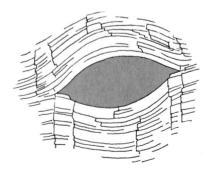

Limestone is found in many marine sedimentary deposits, especially those formed later in the earth's history, and Cretaceous chalk and Carboniferous and Jurassic limestones are well known in southern England. Limestone and chalk deposits on the sea bed depend partly on a strong organic life in the sea and partly on the absence of other sediments. These conditions exist today in the Arabian Gulf and similar areas where the dry climate allows only a small supply of detritus from land. Some limestone creates reefs, as seen in tropical seas where the water is clear and not too deep. Other types of reefs occur in colder water and at greater depths.

Peat, brown coal and coal

Peat, brown coal and coal consist almost entirely of more or less carbonized plant debris. These soft rocks, which cannot stand up to long transport, are brown or black, can be burned and are classified by how far the carbonization has proceeded.

The least decomposed of this group is brown or black peat, made up of well-preserved plant remains. It is so crumbly that it never forms pebbles. Brown coal is more compact, and the plant remains are only partly preserved. This brown or black rock can be made to draw a dark line on paper or porcelain. Lignite, a type of brown coal, has a partly preserved internal structure. Black coal, mostly without preserved plant remains, is often finely layered and gives a black dust. One of its varieties, cannel coal, does not give dust, but is shinier and has a conchoidal fracture. Anthracite, without traces of plant remains, is a hard, shiny, black variety.

Parts of preserved plants may be contained in brownish-black, crumbly or earthy peat

Black coal does not contain identifiable fossilized plants. Some of the fine layers are smudgy matt black and others are shiny

Peat develops in bogs where the normal decomposition of plant fragments is hindered by 'stagnant' conditions. Dead plant remains are normally broken down by oxygen-liking (aerobic) bacteria, but in still (stagnant) water, oxygen is quickly used up and decomposition is taken over by (anaerobic) bacteria which do not need oxygen. They then secrete poisonous matter, which halts further decomposition. This is how plant remains accumulate in coastal swamps or on lagoon bottoms without decomposing.

When this material is buried under further sediments and becomes compressed, soft brown coal develops first and then, with stronger pressure, coal. This process means that the percentage of coal, and therefore the calorific value, increases so that the most compressed is the best quality. Along with this transformation, gases are produced such as methane, the major component of natural gas. The natural gas that occurs, for instance in the southern parts of the North Sea, is generated by deep-lying layers of coal.

In a series of carbonaceous materials there is a gradual change from peat to anthracite. Note how the calorific value rises as the deposit becomes more solidified

	carbon	hydrogen	oxygen	nitrogen	calorific value
	%	%	%	%	therms/tonne
wood	50	6	43	0.9	75–100
peat	55	6	37	1.7	75
brown coal	73	5	21	1.3	130
coal	84	5	9	1.5	275
anthracite	94	3	3	0.9	320

Anthracite forms where heat and compression have been especially strong, either because of nearby volcanic activity or where the coal layers have been subjected to metamorphism and folding in mountain ranges.

The most important coal deposits in northern Europe were formed in the Carboniferous period about 300 million years ago. So many remains of plants and animals have been found in the associated strata, in spite of carbonization, that it has been possible to build up a very detailed picture of life in these primeval swamps. Although deposits older than Carboniferous have been located, coal made up of dead land plants is absent in strata more than 400 million years old. It was at that time that the first land plants began to spread over the earth. Deposits of coal and brown coal younger than Carboniferous are widespread and peat formation has continued right up to the present day, in bogs and swamps.

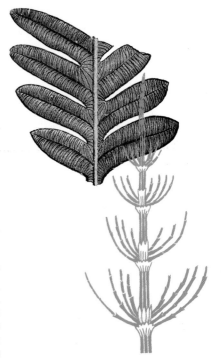

An imprint of a fern (top) from clay partings in coal seams some 300 million years old. There were also giant horse-tails during that period, whose distant descendants can be seen today as modest plants in the woods

Flint, moler and silicified rocks

The rocks in this group are either wholly or largely composed of silica, the same material that, in its most crystalline form, is the mineral quartz. The commonest silica rock among loose pebbles is flint, which is compact, hard, often black but can also be brown or grey. Flint nodules can also be seen in silicified limestone layers. These greyish or white nodules resemble the limestone but have the toughness of flint itself. As concretions flint may take on many surprising shapes, occasionally like animals, although these have nothing to do with fossilization. Nevertheless, flint can replace some fossils, such as sea-urchins, or create a spherical clinking stone. Flint pebbles, such as those on the beaches of Kent and Sussex, can become very cylindrical and often show crescentic fracture marks (chatter marks) because they were battered about by sea waves.

This relatively brittle rock breaks into pieces in a characteristic manner, a conchoidal fracture, when the broken surface is curved with concentric lines like a mussel shell. The facility with which flint can be fractured led to its widespread use by prehistoric man, who manufactured many tools and weapons at places such as Grimes Graves, East Anglia.

49

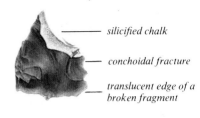

silicified chalk

conchoidal fracture

translucent edge of a
broken fragment

*Flint with silicified chalk. This fragment,
from a larger nodule, indicates some of its
conspicuous characteristics*

*Black flint. Near the centre of the
illustration is a good example of a typical
conchoidal fracture. There are also several
pieces of greyish silicified chalk or
limestone that have not been entirely
transformed into flint. Note also the
imprints of sea-urchins*

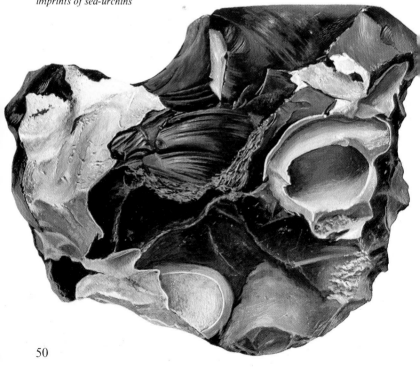

Brown flint may range from darkest red through red-brown to pale yellow. Often it is only the pebble's covering that is tinted – the inside remains grey or black. The red-brown colour is an indication of the surface conditions to which the pebble was exposed. In this case, iron precipitation took place

Grey flint with a black core contains a little residual chalk which would have made it unsuitable for creating tools in primitive times

Moler is a muddy variety of diatomaceous earth, also called Kieselguhr. Compact, pale grey, often finely layered, it resembles clay or mudstone, but it is very light in weight and clearly less dense than, for instance, mudstone. Initially it is soft, but when precipitated chalk is added it becomes a hard cement-stone. Pure diatomaceous earth is similar to moler but is light yellow to whitish and is too soft to form pebbles.

Silicified rocks result from the silica deposits in their pore spaces. Thus a rock, which was originally fairly soft, develops greater hardness without losing its original appearance. Examples are silicified lime-stone and silicified shale. Silicified trees (tree-opal, fossil wood) result when silica completely replaces the original material. They look like normal trees complete with grain and knots, but they are rock hard.

Some flint pieces are silicified lime-stone, where the lime is wholly replaced.

Cross-section of a 'clinking stone'. The remains of a halichondria (Plinthosella resonans) *in the centre makes the stone clink. The surrounding flint nodule is a spherical concretion formed after the death of a sea-urchin*

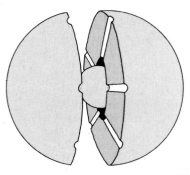

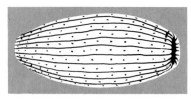

Silica-bearing organisms. Top: halichondria (life-size). Centre and below: microscopic skeletons of radiolaria and diatoms

Black flint with sea-urchin spines. Flint has been deposited inside the empty sea-urchin shell (fossilization) and has also replaced the outer covering of chalk. The shell itself, which consisted of larger calcite crystals, is partly preserved as silicified chalk

Common rocks in the earth's crust contain silica, chiefly in the form of quartz, or in the various silicate minerals such as feldspar. Normally, but not always, quartz resists chemical weathering, whereas feldspar is more easily broken down. Silica, released by this breakdown, is carried away in percolating groundwater to reach rivers, lakes and the sea where it is used by various organisms in the construction of their shells and skeletons. Single-celled siliceous algae (diatoms), that live like plankton in lakes and the sea, have shells of silica, as do single-celled organisms like radiolaria, which live only in salt water. Halichondria skeletons consist of silica needles. When silica-bearing organisms die, their organic parts are broken down – in most cases the silica dissolves and the material is re-used by new organisms. Alternatively, such large quantities of the silica shells sink to the bottom that they create whole deposits. Radiolarian or diatomaceous mud can be found on the deep ocean floor under some conditions. Moler is the deposit of diatom shells, together with clay, near the coast.

The necessary material for flint formation in chalk deposits is in halichondria's needle-shaped skeleton. Silica needles, calcareous mud and shells mix together on the sea floor and become a part of the

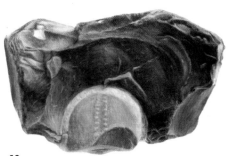

newly-deposited chalk. They soon dissolve in water within the sediment pores, carrying the silica downwards until it precipitates again. The action usually takes place in holes or cracks, but often begins its transformation around solid silica, such as a clump of undissolved needles. With the onset of precipitation, the newly-formed flint nodule attracts more silica and grows larger. In many cases this causes the lime to be dissolved and carried away. Since fine-grained chalk dissolves more

Moler, unusually light in weight, is pale grey and almost compact. The fine layering (lamination) contrasts with the holes made by boring bivalves

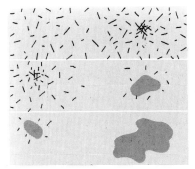

Three stages in flint formation :

Silica needles in newly-deposited chalk

Beginning of concretion formation

On the right, all the silica is now formed into one flint nodule

53

easily than coarse-grained, the smaller fossils in flintstone disappear but the larger calcareous shells remain. Silicified trees develop in a similar way, but under completely different circumstances, particularly if they were buried in feldspar-bearing sand. When exposed to chemical weathering the feldspar is the first to be attacked, releasing silica which dissolves in the sedi-ment's water. As the buried tree rots, silica is re-deposited in its place, preserving even the smallest details of the tree's surface. This fantastic process of gradual transformation from tree to stone is not yet fully understood.

When they are silicified, trees can be perfectly preserved but are nevertheless as hard as flint (fossil wood)

Iron sediments

This group consists of various iron-bearing sediments, some of which are very important as iron ores. Iron is a component of many minerals, but three are of special interest: iron spar (siderite), chamosite and brown ironstone (limonite). Siderite, an iron carbonate, is usually light grey-brown, can be scratched with a knife and bubbles when tested with warm hydrochloric acid. Chamosite is a green iron-bearing silicate mineral most often found as oolites. Rust-coloured brown ironstone, usually from the weathering of iron-bearing rocks, is responsible for the characteristic reddish weathering-crust on the outside of many iron-rich rocks.

Oolitic ironstone and its matrix have a distinctive structure of either siderite or chamosite. Clay ironstone, a mud within which finely-divided iron spar is precipitated, is a massive rock, but often occurs as concretions. Bog iron ore, of brown ironstone, usually originates in swamps, but sometimes there are compact lumps in lakes. Quartz-banded iron ore, of alternating layers of quartz and various iron minerals, forms first as a sediment but later undergoes radical alteration, and is therefore very varied.

Chemical weathering of rocks in the earth's crust releases iron which is then carried in solution in groundwater, especially if the water is oxygen-free or slightly acid. When the groundwater comes to the surface, in springs for example, the iron makes contact with atmospheric oxygen and precipitates as brown ironstone. In many instances, bacteria are associated with this process. Bog iron ore is formed when this precipitation takes place in swamps. The precipitated brown ironstone is often so fine-grained that it remains suspended in water to be carried via rivers out to sea where the salt water causes all the small particles to coagulate, fall to the bottom, and form deposits of iron oxide.

The acid and oxygen-free bottom water in fjords and bays dissolves brown ironstone. Under certain conditions this re-dissolved iron may become chamosite, iron spar or iron pyrites, and thus integrates into marine deposits. In some cases it forms oolitic ironstone and in others clay ironstone.

Conglomerate with brown ironstone is formed when iron-rich percolating waters coat small pebbles with iron oxide (limonite)

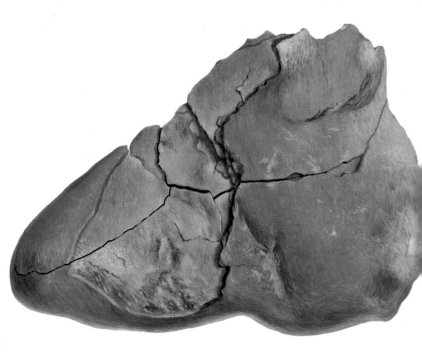

This clay-ironstone concretion was originally an iron spar deposit in a sandy mudstone. The iron spar later altered the outer parts to limonite, giving the stone its rust-coloured weathered crust

Oolitic ironstone which has been exposed to such severe weathering that the original material in both oolites and matrix have become brown ironstone and red haematite. The drawing is twice natural size

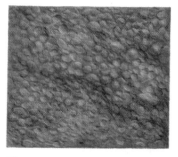

All of the quartz-banded iron ores developed early in the earth's history, more than 2,000 million years ago. The exact mechanism of formation is unknown, but it is believed that the atmosphere was nearly free of oxygen, and this would have been an important factor.

Iron is a common material in the earth's crust and, bearing in mind that under certain conditions it dissolves in water and under others precipitates out, it is not surprising that there were iron-bearing sedimentary deposits in all geological eras. These have been of special importance in casting light on how the earth's atmosphere developed. As already mentioned, banded ironstones originated before the atmosphere got its present-day oxygen content. About 1,800 million years ago, red sandstone appeared for the first time but it becomes more common in later iron deposits. Red coloration characterizes 'brown' ironstone and haematite, the even more oxidized iron material. The appearance of red-coloured sandstone could mean that the atmospheric oxygen content at that time was high enough to convert dissolved iron into brown ironstone and haematite.

Laterite, bauxite and kaolin

Laterite closely resembles bauxite. Both are red-brown to yellowish-red, and may be either crumbly or very hard, with an earthy or pisolitic structure. Laterite shows vermiform growths as well as pisolites. Kaolin, a whitish clay rock (fireclay, china clay) contains clay and a proportion of quartz grains.

These three rock types are formed chiefly by chemical weathering in tropical regions. The high temperature and considerable rainfall can cause extensive disintegration of common rocks such as granite and basalt. Only the iron and/or aluminium compounds are left behind – the rest washes away. The residual rocks, laterite, bauxite and kaolin, are the weathering residues formed in this way. Iron compounds predominate in laterite: it seems that such rocks result from percolated water that is not too acid, or when the iron-rich rocks are weathered. As a rule, laterite has only a moderate content of aluminium compounds, but bauxite results when the major portion is aluminium. Bauxite is normally produced by the weathering of feldspathic rocks such as granite or gneiss, when the percolating water is acid. The china clay from kaolin, formed in a similar way, is extensively used in the pottery industry.

Kaolin is white, soft and crumbly. It is created by the deep weathering of granite (china clay granite) and can therefore contain grains of unaltered quartz

Bauxite, which varies from yellow-red to brown-red, is very soft, with scattered small spherical pisolites

pisolites

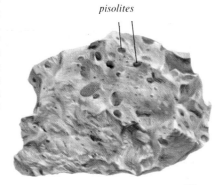

Concretions

A concretion is a lump within a rock. It is almost safe to say that it is 'born' as a pebble because it doesn't first have to be broken down or ground away. Concretions are often either spherical or lens-shaped and, when two or more grow together, some very strange outlines can result. Some examples may have bizarre shapes, but they are rather rare. Colour and external appearance are decided by the basic content, but there are usually two distinguishing characteristics: either the concretion consists of only one material, normally a mineral, or it is formed by mineral precipitation and is therefore of at least two kinds, the precipitate and the host rock. Even so, it may be impossible to identify the two types if the surrounding rock is too compact.

Many different minerals form concretions. For instance, pyrite concretions can be yellow, but the rich iron content of the weathered outer crust may make them rust-coloured. The interior is often very coarse-grained, with a radial ray-like structure. They look heavier and 'foreign' among other stones, which is why they are often mistaken for meteorites.

Flint is mainly found as concretions in chalk. Desert-rose is not really a concretion, although it develops in the same way: it is the mineral gypsum with petal-like crystals pointing upwards. Gypsum is white or pale, and can be scratched with a fingernail.

There are many calcite concretions – 'pure', like antrakonite balls, loess-dolls, or mixed, like sandstone. Irregularly-shaped loess-dolls are a feature of the loess deposits in

A flint nodule which may look like a baby seal, but the shape is purely accidental and has nothing to do with a fossil

central Europe. Sandstone concretions are made up of sand bonded together by calcite. Although often spherical, they look like sandstone.

Exterior and cross-section of pyrite concretions. The yellow colour, density (pyrite has a density of 5) and the radiating structure are characteristic

Clay-ironstone concretions are clay or, at times, fine-grained sand knitted together by iron spar. They are light reddish-yellow or greyish, but may often have a dark rust-coloured weathered crust which is harder than the paler interior.

Phosphate concretions are dark greenish or green-black outside but often with a light brown inside. They mainly comprise the phosphate mineral apatite and calcite in a compact or very fine-grained form, sometimes with sand grains or other

Sandstone concretions look like spheres of sandstone. The different grain sizes depend on the type of sandstone in which the concretion took place

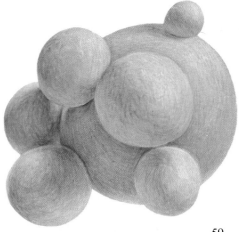

Phosphate concretions are pebbles and clots of phosphate knitted together with a phosphatic matrix

rock material. They often contain shells, teeth or bone pieces which are wholly or partly converted to phosphate.

Concretions develop by means of a diagenetic process which takes place after sediment deposition. Their basic make-up is most often present in newly-formed sediment characterized by its low percentage of finely-divided small particles. Sandstone may, for example, contain small amounts of finely-divided calcium carbonate. When the concretion-forming processes occur these small grains dissolve in pore water in the rock and the material is later re-deposited as concretions.

Metamorphic rocks

A loose sediment develops into a hard sedimentary rock during the processes of diagenesis which set in immediately after formation, but become more and more thorough the deeper it is buried under newer sediments. This happens partly because the sediment is increasingly pressed together by the weight of the overlying rocks, and partly because temperature rises as depth increases. However, the diagenesis changes are not so complete that the sedimentary identity is lost. This only occurs if the rock is subjected to still higher temperature, greater pressure and, eventually, also deformation. Then new and stable minerals replace the original ones to create a whole new rock. When such a re-crystallization takes place the rock is said to be metamorphosed, and is called metamorphic.

All three main rock groups – sedimentary, metamorphic and igneous – can be altered by the metamorphic processes outlined on p. 20. Varying degrees of alteration can occur, although the rocks remain essentially solid and usually retain some primary characteristics. An exception is the hybrid rock migmatite, a case where a pre-existing metamorphic rock may lose all its primary characteristics when invaded by granitic material.

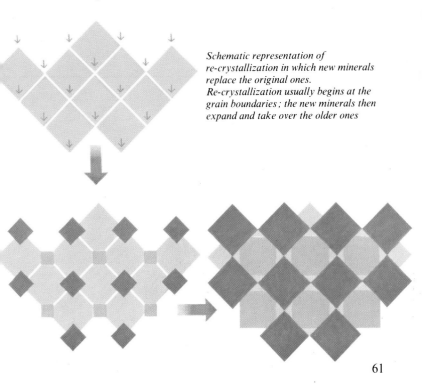

Schematic representation of re-crystallization in which new minerals replace the original ones.
Re-crystallization usually begins at the grain boundaries; the new minerals then expand and take over the older ones

It is a proven fact that re-crystallization from increasing temperature and pressure takes place much more easily than re-crystallization resulting from decreasing temperature and pressure. Thus a metamorphic rock stays 'frozen' with the minerals formed when the pressure and temperature were highest. For example, if you study a series of metamorphic specimens which were originally surface rocks, such as sediments and lavas, and which have again surfaced as a result of land upheaval and erosion, you note that the series has been subject to certain pressure and temperature changes.

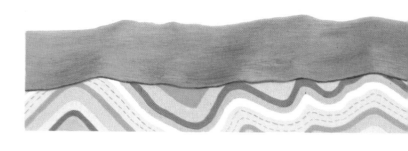

migmatite

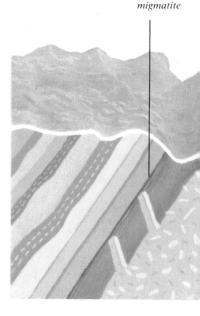

Section through a fold range. The relatively weakly deformed and metamorphosed rocks are at the upper left. At the top right, the more deformed and altered rocks are thrust over the remainder. This large overthrust body is also called a nappe. The most deformed rocks from the centre of the mountain range are at the bottom

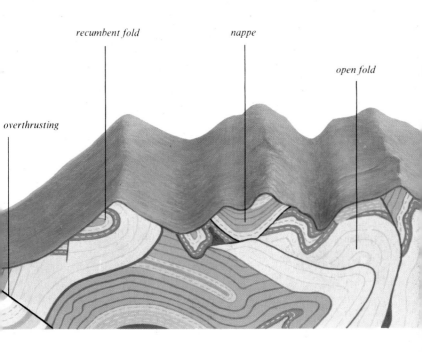

overthrusting   *recumbent fold*   *nappe*   *open fold*

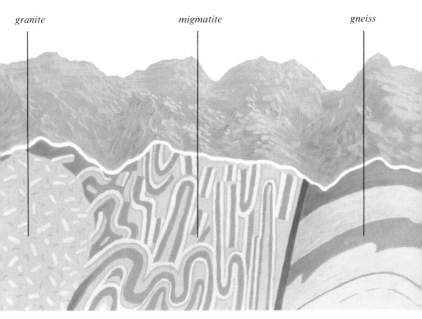

granite   *migmatite*   *gneiss*

63

Quartzite is nearly colourless because it is almost entirely quartz. When broken the fracture passes through the quartz grains (see p. 36), suggesting that this is a meta-quartzite. There are no elongated minerals which would make it schistose

The first occurred when the series was buried under younger rocks. As temperature and pressure increased, further metamorphism took place. Temperature and pressure finally fell again as the rock approached the earth's surface once more. If the minerals always adapted to the conditions, the end product would have been the same as the original rock, but since re-crystallization is very difficult when temperature and pressure fall, the minerals remained as they were when temperature and pressure were highest. The upper and lower layers of very thick strata do not reach the same high temperature and pressure. They therefore re-crystallize into different rock types, depending on the change in conditions at various levels in the strata. This is only an ideal situation because a thick rock series will invariably be of different types. Even though they are metamorphosed under the same conditions, these will create differing metamorphic rocks. For example, there can be layers of sandstone and layers of chalk in a metamorphosed rock series. The sandstone layers are almost entirely mineral quartz grains with a chemical composition of nearly 100% silica. Quartz is the only mineral with such a composition, so the rocks will always be made of it.

Metamorphism only closes the rock's pore spaces. In this case, as with diagenesis, there is very little difference between a sedimentary quartzite and a true metamorphic quartzite. One cannot even tell whether a quartzite was formed under low or high temperature and pressure conditions. Limestone behaves in roughly the same way as sandstone. The sedimentary structures disappear with re-crystallization but no new minerals appear. A metamorphosed limestone is marble, which will almost invariably be composed of calcite only if the original limestone was pure. If, on the other hand, the limestone contained dolomite or other 'impurities' such as sand grains or clay particles, there is the possibility of a chemical reaction and thus the formation of new minerals in the marble. Stellate marble, with radiating crystals of a silicate mineral such as amphibole, is an example of a metamorphosed 'impure' limestone. Obviously the original will have an important effect on the appearance of the new metamorphic rock. The chemical composition of the original determines its mineral content, but it is the conditions during metamorphism, especially pressure and temperature, that actually decide which ones they become.

polished face

white marble

Marble is mainly calcite and therefore bubbles when tested with cold hydrochloric acid. Technically it is a limestone that can be polished, but geologically it is limestone re-crystallized during metamorphism. When this occurs, the remains of any organisms disappear and there is a transformation into a crystalline form which, like quartzite, can be of an interlocking texture. The marble's colour comes from its various impurities. A small amount of iron results in a reddish shade, while copper turns it greenish

red marble

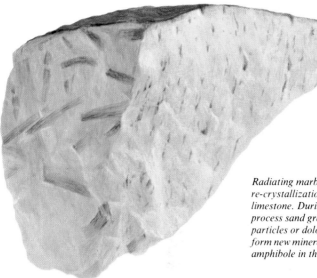

Radiating marble is the re-crystallization of impure limestone. During this process sand grains, mud particles or dolomite react to form new minerals such as the amphibole in this example

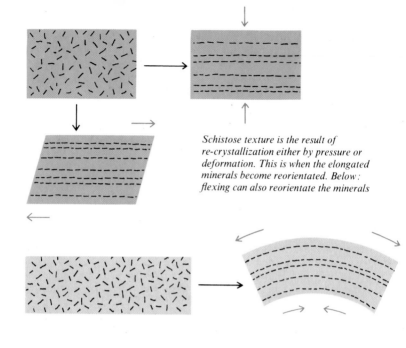

Schistose texture is the result of re-crystallization either by pressure or deformation. This is when the elongated minerals become reorientated. Below: flexing can also reorientate the minerals

The different kinds of deformation also affect the appearance of metamorphic rocks. Schistosity, a characteristic of the majority, is due to deformation. Imagine a rock re-crystallizing under the weight of overlying strata: it is subjected to vertical compression and will flatten with severe pressure. Under these conditions some minerals grow against the pressure. The majority, however, grow out sideways where there is less resistance, and develop a schistose texture and perhaps also a cleavage, so that the rock splits into thin flakes along these planes of weakness. Another type of deformation is a smearing-out, in which the original minerals turn to lie parallel to the 'smearing direction' or, in certain cases, at an angle to it. Again the result is a schistose texture. This flattening is a very common kind of deformation, since most metamor-phic rocks are folded, and strata folding is almost always accompanied by a smearing-out.

Thus the appearance of a metamorphic rock depends on three factors: the composition of the original rock that decides which minerals can possibly form; the conditions during re-crystallization which decide the minerals that actually form; and the deformation which creates the rock's texture and structure.

Metamorphic rocks can be divided into three major groups: rocks that developed under high temperature but low pressure (contact metamorphism); rocks metamorphosed chiefly by high pressure (dynamic metamorphism); and those where the metamorphism involved both high pressure and high temperature (regional metamorphism).

Contact metamorphism

Contact metamorphism is a change or re-crystallization that is due simply to heating up. For example, a lava which flows over a clay deposit causes heating of the clay which will, in certain cases, change to a brick-like rock (baked schist). Such a rock is formed by 'burning' in exactly the same way clay is burned to form bricks in a brick works. In addition to this baking on the surface, the up-welling lava heats the surrounding rocks on its way to the surface and causes further contact metamorphism. Spotted slates and hornfels are the most important rocks created by this method.

Spotted slates and hornfels

Spotted slate resembles shale except for its mineral spots, which are small, irregular and rather spongy markings, often of carbon. With stronger metamorphism the spots change into recognizable mineral grains such as mica. Contact metamorphosed rocks are not deformed, so that any positioning of the spots is inherited from the original sedimentary rock. With more thorough re-crystallization, however, it changes into the compact rock hornstone or hornfels, named after its similarity to ornamental stag horn. The usually dark colour can show a slightly blurred banding with purple, red or greenish layers and the breaks reveal a velvety lustre. Some examples may have visible crystals of, for example, mica or garnet in a re-crystallized compact groundmass.

Spotted slates and hornfels are created, therefore, when clays and marls come into contact with hot molten rock. The most important effect is heating, but gases from the magma may also change the rock by reacting with it as they pass through and escape to the surface.

Rocks formed by contact metamorphism occur in a zone, from a few metres to several kilometres wide, around the hot, solidifying,

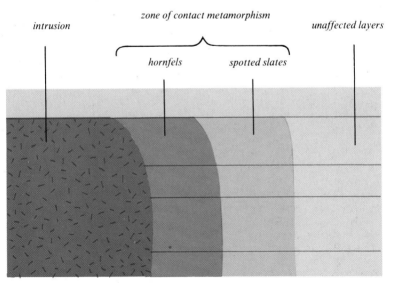

intrusion   *zone of contact metamorphism*   *unaffected layers*

hornfels   *spotted slates*

Hornstone, a compact rock, often has irregular and indistinct layers similar to the texture of stag horn

magmatic rock. The zone's breadth depends on how much heat the passing magma gives up, but at most it amounts to only a modest volume. Contact metamorphic rocks are therefore relatively uncommon and their pebbles are not easy to find. Pebbles of marble – limestone changed by contact metamorphism – are a noteworthy discovery.

Fine-grained spotted slates have spots of dark andalusite

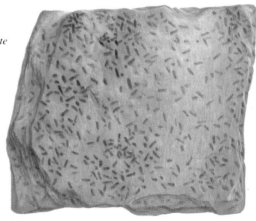

Dynamic metamorphism

Rocks are deformed by increased pressure or tension. If the affecting force is not too great, and if it continues over a long period, deformation makes the rocks behave like a very viscous fluid and they become folded. With stronger or more rapidly increasing force the rock's strength is exceeded, ruptures occur and deformation takes place along the fracture lines. Fracture zones reveal a great deal of crushing, and perhaps also some actual melting from frictional heat. Breccia and mylonite are the two most important examples of dynamic metamorphism, also called crushing metamorphism.

Breccia and mylonite

Breccia is composed of angular rock pieces held together by a matrix material, usually quartz. Thus it is coarse-grained and resembles a conglomerate. Mylonite can occur as an entire pebble or merely as a vein within one. It is either hard, fine-grained and quite compact or has small, more or less rounded grains in a compressed groundmass (mortar structure). Usually light greenish, it can be faintly banded in paler and slightly darker strips. Occasionally you will see a polished surface on a stone. This may be a slickenside, which is formed when rocks are ground against each other along a fault.

Breccia. A fault breccia with bits of a pale rock are held together by a greenish-black material and cut through by quartz veins

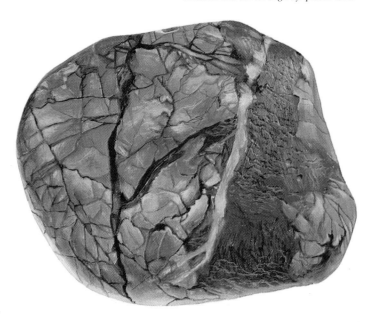

Breccia can also form by sedimentation, as a conglomerate with angular particles. Sedimentary breccia differs from crush breccia in that it contains grains of many different rock types.

Breccia and mylonite are created when a stressed rock breaks into pieces. If this deformation is relatively weak, the rock breaks up only slightly and breccia is formed by gradual in-filling of the cracks.

Slickenside. This stone was part of one side of a fault (see below). When the two sides of the fault moved, they polished the rock. The grooves often suggest the direction of the fault's movement

mylonite vein

gneiss

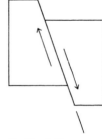

Faulting is the movement of two rock masses in relation to each other

Mylonite in gneiss. The actual mylonite vein is compact with greenish and various light colours. Note the remains of partly crushed gneiss in the vein

Mylonite results when more intense deformation crushes the material to a fine-grain size which then becomes either knitted, or perhaps fused, together by frictional heat.

Dynamic metamorphism takes place at relatively shallow depths in the earth's crust. The increasing pressure and higher temperature at greater depths cause the rock to deform like a fluid.

As in the case of rocks formed by contact metamorphism, those formed by crushing at fault-lines are relatively uncommon, so that their pebbles are rarely found, especially those exhibiting slickensides – not to be confused with glacially striated pebbles which are more commonplace.

Regional metamorphism

In contrast to the localized mechanics of contact and dynamic metamorphism, regional metamorphism is on a grand scale because it is an integral part of mountain building.

The greatest percentage of our metamorphic rocks are formed in this way, when material of the continental shelf and margin is subjected to considerable deformation while, at the same time, gradual land upheaval changes what was once the sea floor into high mountains. All of this proceeds so slowly that it can take 100 million years or more to build up a whole range.

This type of metamorphism results not only from intense deformation but also from heating up during mountain building. The initial rocks are mainly deposits from the continental shelf – sandstone, clay and limestone – and from the continental margin – greywacke and various rocks of volcanic origin. The total thickness of these sediments and volcanic rocks can be over 10 km, so that the entire series may be changed, partly by pressures due to mountain building and partly by the depth of burial. Throughout a very thick series of rocks there will be marked differences of temperature and pressure during metamorphism.

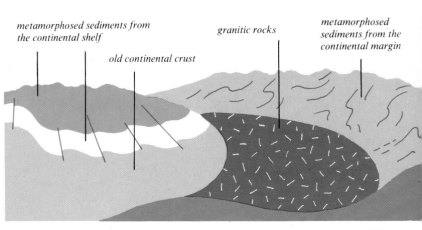

metamorphosed sediments from the continental shelf

old continental crust

granitic rocks

metamorphosed sediments from the continental margin

metamorphic grade	sandstone	limestone	mudstone	clay	basic lava
low	quartzite	marble	slate	slate	greenstone
medium	quartzite	marble	mica schist	amphibolite	amphibolite
high	quartzite	marble	gneiss	amphibolite	amphibolite

In general, heat and pressure will be greatest in the deepest, central parts of the developing range, and will diminish upwards and outwards to either flank. The variation manifests itself in the finished metamorphic rocks – the highest and outermost ones are those which have been metamorphosed at relatively low pressures and temperatures, but those nearer the centre of the range have been subjected to substantially higher pressures and temperatures. This difference corresponds to low-grade and high-grade metamorphism, respectively. At the lower metamorphic grades there are the slates, greenschists and soapstone, while the crystalline schists and gneisses are products of high-grade metamorphism. Where the high temperature has partly melted the material, migmatite occurs. Granitic rocks ultimately form in the depths where most of the material has been melted (anatexis).

Slates, phyllites, greenschists and soapstone

Slate is a compact rock, with well-developed fissility. It can be black, but light greenish and purplish shades are not uncommon. Slate resembles shale, a sedimentary rock. A weak fissility appears during deposition in shale and it may, therefore, be split parallel with the bedding layers. In slates, however, cleavage develops during metamorphism, mainly due to pressures which are not necessarily at right angles to the layering. Thus cleavage and bedding in slates are not usually parallel. This phenomenon (oblique cleavage) is best illustrated in slates.

Phyllite, a very fine-grained schistose rock, has shiny surfaces

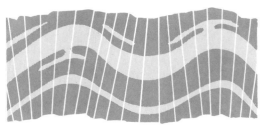

Above: cleavage planes in a folded mountain massif. The layers, originally of shales, have been folded by lateral compression. At the same time, re-crystallization has transformed the layers into slate with transverse cleavage planes crossing the bedding

Below: pale green slate, side view (left) and front view (right). Note how the cleavage planes (vertical lines) run across the oblique coloured bands of the original layering. This phenomenon is called transverse cleavage

There are some kinds of slaty rocks which are fine-grained but not necessarily compact. In phyllite (clay-mica schist), the shiny cleavage planes are due to the growth of small bronze, greenish or green-black mica flakes. Greenschist is greenish, talc schist is greyish or greenish white and both look 'muddy'. Their minerals are very soft; talc schist in particular can be scratched with a fingernail. Green-stone and soapstone are similar to greenschist and talc schist but do not exhibit cleavage.

Rocks in this group represent the lowest grades of regional metamorphism. Slate, phyllite and certain greenschists are altered clay sediments. In slate the primary influence is pressure, which causes flat minerals to re-crystallize with their flat surfaces perpendicular to the greatest pressure, thus producing the charac-

Greenschist. Very fine-grained, weakly folded schistose rock with layers of greenish micaceous mineral and pale layers with, among other materials, the soft mineral talc

teristic cleavage. New minerals, especially the micaceous ones, replace the clay minerals of the original sediment in phyllite and the greenschists.

Greenstone and certain types of greenschist result mainly from the metamorphism of basalt and are more or less cleaved depending on the strength of the deformation. Soapstone and talc schist are formed from material especially rich in the element magnesium – for example, by metamorphism of peridotite. These low-grade metamorphic rocks make up large sections of many of the world's mountain ranges.

Crystalline schists

Crystalline schists are rocks which display clear schistose texture and a strong fissility. However, the latter is seldom as perfect as the planar cleavage in slates, and there is often a folded or wavy fissility that causes irregular splitting, making it useless as a roofing material.

Mica schist is crystalline schist with a large mica content but the terms biotite schist, muscovite schist, or even two-mica schist are also used according to which one is predominant, or whether both are present in roughly equal amounts.

Mica schist with tightly folded layers consisting chiefly of large muscovite flakes

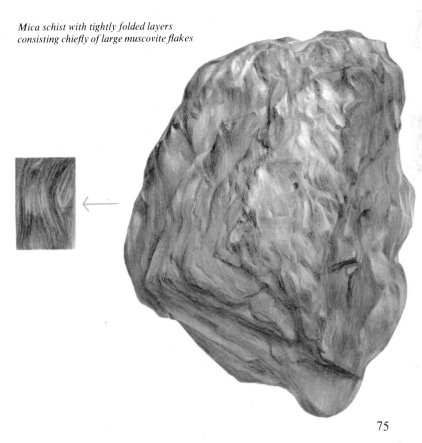

There are large crystals of the red mineral garnet in garnet-mica schist

Quartz and feldspar are common constituents, but mica schist's colour is decided by whether dark or light mica predominates. If the quartz content is sufficiently large, it is a quartzitic schist (mica quartzite).

Mica schist with crystals of the commonest red mineral, garnet, is a garnet-mica schist.

The mineral amphibole is the largest component of the other crystalline schists, termed am-

The texture of garnet amphibolite is clearly schistose with characteristic pale feldspars. There are also large clumps of small garnet crystals

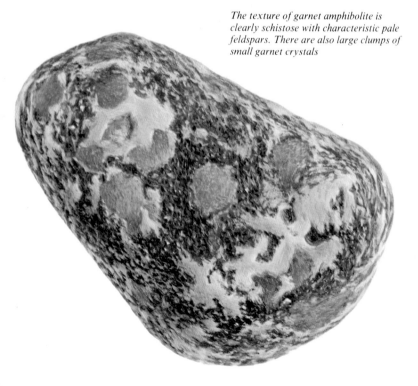

Amphibolite (hornblende schist) is black and coarse-grained with a clear schistose texture (in the direction of the arrow) and marked fissility

phibolites. The dark amphibole minerals are more or less tapered and sometimes needle-shaped, thus amphibolite is dark with a schistose texture, but with a weaker fissility than mica schist. When garnet is present it is a garnet amphibolite, while hornblende is the most important mineral in hornblende schist.

Crystalline schists are formed at higher metamorphic grades than slate and greenstone. Clay is transformed under these conditions to mica schist which, at the higher metamorphic grades, can contain garnet. Muddy sandstone recrystallizes to quartzitic schist. The original material for the formation of amphibolite can be of two quite different types, marl or basaltic rock. It is impossible to tell from casually examining a pebble which material was the original. The presence of garnet again signifies that a high metamorphic grade has been reached.

Crystalline schists are commonly found in mountain-root zones, areas worn down to the deep roots of old mountain ranges.

Gneiss and gneissic types

The most important characteristic of a gneiss is its stripy appearance. Layers, mainly made up of mica or amphibole with a clear schistose texture, alternate with those chiefly of granular minerals like quartz and feldspar which do not have such a pronounced schistose texture. Gneiss differs from crystalline schist in that it is not schistose throughout, and by its often irregular banding or striping.

If the layers are thin, it is a stripy gneiss, but if they are broader it is banded, while irregular streaks (schlieren) produce the schlieric gneiss. Augen gneiss has 'eyes' of feldspar or of feldspar and quartz, around which the gneiss layers are draped. Gneiss can also be characterized by its most conspicuous mineral, biotite or garnet gneiss, or two descriptions can be combined, for instance, to give banded muscovite gneiss, or schlieric hornblende gneiss.

Gneiss forms at about the same metamorphic grade as crystalline schist. Whether the rock is a gneiss or a schist depends on its mica content. There are several types of gneiss striping or banding; in some cases the banding reflects a layering in the original rock, such as alternating layers of sand and clay, or because these rocks have been subjected to much stronger deformation. We know that elongated minerals such as amphibole become orientated to lie parallel during deformation. They can also be concentrated in certain zones in the rock which

Right: folded gneiss is light grey with thin pale 'bands' folded on an 'axis' parallel to its length. Each band appears several times on the surface

Below: in striped gneiss the thin striping results from alternating layers of amphibolites and granites

then take on a stripy look. In the
same way a granite can, with deformation, become 'striped granite'
or a gneiss.

Gneiss is found in northwestern
Scotland, especially in the Outer
Hebrides, in Scandinavia and in all
mountain-root areas where, together
with crystalline schist and granite, it
makes up the three commonest
rocks.

*Right: light-coloured garnet gneiss is
striped with dark minerals which are
sometimes clumps of dark amphiboles
or red garnets*

*Below: pale gneiss has thin amphibolite
slivers and large phenocryst-like
amphibole crystals*

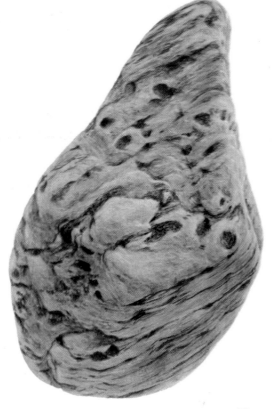

Migmatite is gneiss with granite layers. The gneiss is obviously schistose but the granite layers are granitic. These layers were later offset by a small fault

Migmatite

Migmatite, a 'mixed' rock, consists of material with schistose and granitic textures. The first is commonly gneissic, while the second is obviously granitic – almost entirely of quartz, feldspar and mica. The granitic material occurs as irregular veins or schlieren, or as 'patches' or regular veins cutting the gneiss banding.

Migmatite is the result of such high temperatures during metamorphism that the rock begins to melt. There is then some melt composed of granitic magma, almost regardless of the kind of rock.

Below: how granitic magma forms. Left: the gneiss, with two amphibolite layers, is cut through by a joint. Centre: during metamorphism, the temperature rises so high that the gneiss begins to melt. Right: the resulting magma seeps into the joint, forcing it to open. The granite vein is preserved when the whole mass cools down

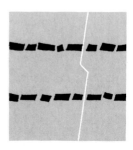
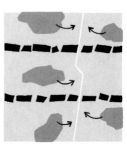

Granitic 'drops' first form within the rock, which sometimes then solidify to granite as the temperature falls. Or, the 'drops' may coalesce into slightly larger magma bodies which flow into cracks and solidify in the surrounding gneiss to become cross-cutting veins.

A characteristic constituent of mountain-root zones, migmatites form a transitional zone between gneiss and crystalline schist on the one hand and the still deeper granitic rocks on the other.

Migmatite with paler granite lenses. Along the boundary between granite and gneiss is a concentration of dark minerals left behind when the paler ones melted to granitic magma

Left: newly-formed granitic magma is often seen between the remnants of amphibolite layers which were broken up during deformation

Below right: 'granite droplets' solidified in position. Note the remains of the dark layers in the granite

Right: a concentration of unmelted minerals may create the dark rim of a granitic body

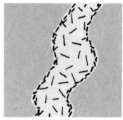

Igneous rocks

The granite problem

Granites are among the most common of the igneous rocks. They are light-coloured, coarse-grained and are composed essentially of quartz, feldspar and mica. Two kinds of feldspar determine the colour: a reddish, flesh-coloured alkaline variety and a yellow to greyish plagioclase. The commonest mica mineral is biotite, but there may also be muscovite and sometimes hornblende (amphibole).

Granitic rocks are divided by grain size into the fine-grained aplite, the coarse-grained granite and the extremely coarse-grained pegmatite. Pegmatite is mainly quartz and feldspar, which sometimes grow together so that the quartz stands out on the feldspar surface like writing. This phenomenon is termed graphic granite. Another coarse-grained granite type is rapakivi granite, with large, often rounded feldspar grains of alkali feldspar crystals surrounded by pale plagioclase rims.

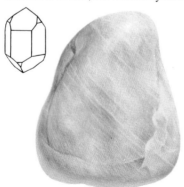

Vein quartz. The quartz crystals in pegmatite and quartz veins may be so large that they constitute whole, slightly pink and semi-transparent pebbles. Vein quartz differs from quartzite in that it consists of only a few large grains

The mineralogical composition of granitic rocks may vary. Where mica predominates, it is biotite or muscovite granite. If the content includes hornblende or pyroxene it is hornblende or pyroxene granite. The alkali feldspar content in true granite is greater than that of the plagioclase. If, however, the quantities of these two feldspars are about the same, the rock is a granodiorite.

Aplite is a fine-grained, 'sugary' textured granitic rock. In this specimen the lower right area is aplite and the remainder granite

Part of a pegmatite vein in gneiss. In addition to the reddish feldspar crystals and white quartz grains, there is often a large mica flake in the middle

Medium-grained pale granite with a reddish, flesh-coloured feldspar (orthoclase)

But if plagioclase is the main component, it is a quartz diorite. It is often impossible to determine the feldspar proportions in a pebble without special apparatus, which is why these rock types are usually described simply as granite.

Most granites develop like the granitic part of migmatite – by partial melting of gneiss and crystalline schist followed by re-crystallization on cooling. Melting is only partial in a mountain range's migmatite zone, but at greater depths it becomes so pervasive that all the rocks melt into granite. Granitic

Hornblende granite. Dark, medium-grained granite with hornblende as its main dark mineral. The dark minerals in granite may be difficult to identify. Try to distinguish between them on the basis of their hardness and cleavage (p. 24)

magma – with a lower density than the unmelted rock left behind – tries to push up in the same way a mushroom thrusts through the soil. We know·that gneisses and crystalline schists surrounding this pushed-up granite mass are often bent outwards, away from the granite. In any case, the movement must stop somewhere and it is rare that a granitic magma reaches all the way to the earth's surface. When this does happen it forms a rhyolite volcano.

Rapakivi granite is a porphyry-like coarse-grained granite rock. It can be identified by its large feldspar grains with pale rims which are usually more deeply weathered in the centre

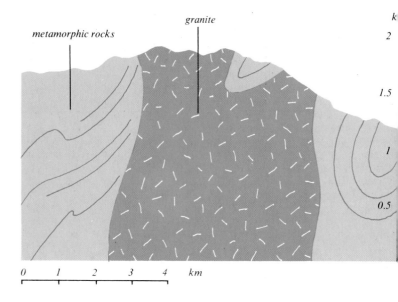

metamorphic rocks   *granite*

1.5

1

0.5

0   1   2   3   4   *km*

A magma's composition depends on how great a proportion of the original rock was melted. The first-formed melt will probably be composed of true granite, but later, if a greater proportion of the rock melts, the magma composition will be more varied. When crystallization occurs granodiorite and quartz diorite, or even diorite and syenite, may result.

The grain size of the granitic end-product depends on the rate of solidification. If crystallization is slow, only relatively few crystals will form, which have time to grow into pegmatite. Aplite, on the other hand, is a product of quick crystallization: so many crystal nuclei appear that they do not have time to grow very large.

Granitic rocks are extremely common in mountain-root zones. The numerous granites of the Scottish Grampians represent the roots of the ancient Caledonian mountain range (400 million years old).

Intruded granite in a mountain massif, when a large granite mass forces the layers in surrounding rocks upwards and outwards

Although granite is one of the commonest rocks it is nevertheless only one of the igneous rocks. Thus, to place it in its context we must examine the various ways in which other igneous rocks are formed.

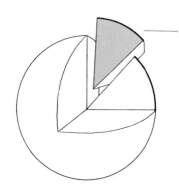

How igneous rocks form

Ancient man believed that there were fiery molten masses in the earth's interior which came to the surface during volcanic eruptions. Today we know that the earth's interior is not, in fact, molten except for the innermost core. Certainly it becomes hotter at depth, but at the same time there are usually enough pressure increases to prevent the material from melting. Under particular conditions, for instance with gneisses, melting occurs to form magma (molten material) which then makes its way to the surface, bursting out in a volcano and flowing as lava.

We have noted that the temperature during mountain range formation can rise to such levels that the rocks begin to melt into a granitic magma, but that this rarely reaches the earth's surface. The most common lava type on the surface is basaltic magma, which forms deep down in the outer part of the earth's mantle which is a layer between the core and the crust. The mantle material is in constant but slow motion, allowing currents of warm material to move into the outer boundary area. This kind of convection causes partial melting so that the molten material works its way to the surface to manifest itself as a volcano. Mauna Loa in Hawaii and Hekla in Iceland are examples of

A section through the earth indicates the thicknesses of the earth's 'shells' and temperatures at the various depths

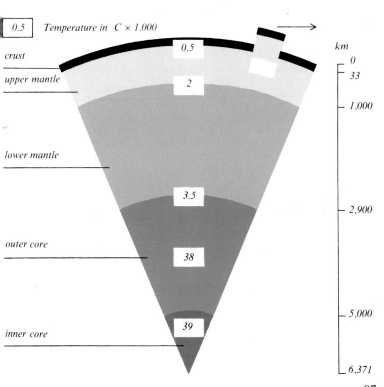

0.5 *Temperature in C × 1,000*

crust 0.5

upper mantle 2

lower mantle 3.5

outer core 38

inner core 39

km
0
33
1,000
2,900
5,000
6,371

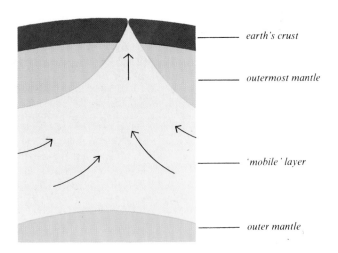

earth's crust

outermost mantle

'mobile' layer

outer mantle

Section through the earth's outer layers. The crust and mantle covering make up the earth's loose outer shell. It is divided into large plates which 'float' on the 'mobile' layer in the mantle

There are two kinds of material in the earth's crustal structure: the continental crust, which builds the continents and underlies the continental shelf sediments, and the ocean-floor crust, under the deep oceans

volcanoes that come from such currents in the mantle. There is also another type of volcanic activity in Iceland, in which fluid basaltic magma flows out from enormous fissures which criss-cross the surface, but from which there is little explosive activity.

In the upper mantle, at depths between 100 km and about 175 km, there is a fluid mobile layer of a very small amount of molten material. The layers over it 'float' as if the earth had a loose shell. This loose outer shell, divided into plates, consists at the present time of six very

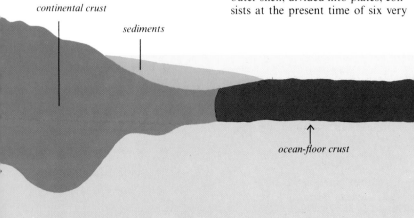

continental crust

sediments

ocean-floor crust

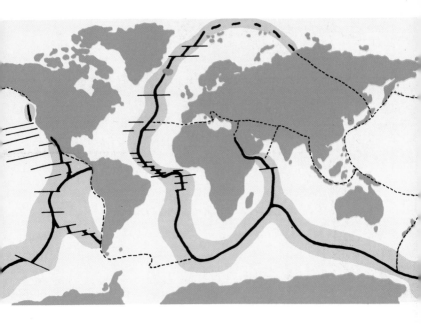

large and about twenty smaller plates which always move in relation to each other as if they were ice-floes on the sea – away from each other in some places and closer together in others. Plate movement is a vital element in the earth's surface appearance and in the creation of volcanic rocks. The formation of basaltic magma is closely related to places where two plates move apart. In fact, basaltic magma from the mantle's mobile layer rises up and fills the 'split' between two separating plates, which widens concurrently with the separation. Sometimes the split initiates within a large continent and the two halves then drift away from each other (continental drift).

An incipient ocean, such as the Red Sea, envelops the split (rift), which is itself floored with a bed of basaltic material, the ocean-floor crust. Thus, outpourings of lava happen mostly beneath the ocean's surface. In most of the world's oceans this rift, with its associated

The plate boundaries in the earth's outer shell are marked by ocean ridges (thick lines) and deep trench zones and major fault-lines (dotted lines)

Section through an ocean ridge. Material from the 'mobile' layer thrusts upwards between two plates, which then move apart. The partly-melted material forms basaltic magma

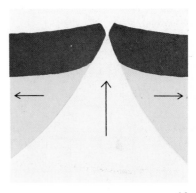

89

Above: basalt. Boulders of this dark, fine-grained rock may sometimes be identified by their five-sided shape, inherited from the distinctive columns (below) which form during cooling of a lava flow

Below: section through a mid-ocean ridge which rises more than 2,000 m above the ocean floor and is often characterized by a marked central rift valley. The section illustrated is approximately 800 km wide

basalts, lies in the middle of a high mid-ocean ridge, such as that beneath the central Atlantic. The only place where such a ridge now stands above the sea surface is in Iceland.

The formation of new ocean-floor crust at mid-ocean ridges is simultaneous with the plate separation on either side (sea-floor spreading). If the two plates create continents, as for example Europe and America on opposite sides of the Atlantic Ocean, the continents move away from each other at a maximum rate estimated at about 6 cm per year.

The formation of another important type of igneous rock, andesitic magma, is also closely related to plate movement in the earth's loose shell, but it occurs

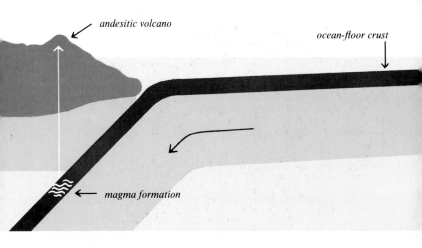

andesitic volcano

ocean-floor crust

magma formation

where two plates move towards one another. When these two plates eventually collide, the crust on one side bends and moves under the other, forcing most of the basaltic ocean crust back down into the mantle along with some sea-floor sediments. The result is a deep submarine trench on the surface, such as the Philippines trench in the Pacific Ocean, where one plate has moved under another. These two plates violently grinding together generate frictional heat high enough to start partial melting of the descending material. Andesitic magma originates in this way, bringing about the volcanoes that are always associated with these deep trenches, for instance in the Andes of South America, or the island arcs of Japan.

Formation of andesitic magma. One plate slides underneath another in a deep trench. At depth, partial melting affects the downward-moving oceanic crust. The magma is andesitic

Andesite is the most typical lava associated with the earth's deep trench vulcanicity

91

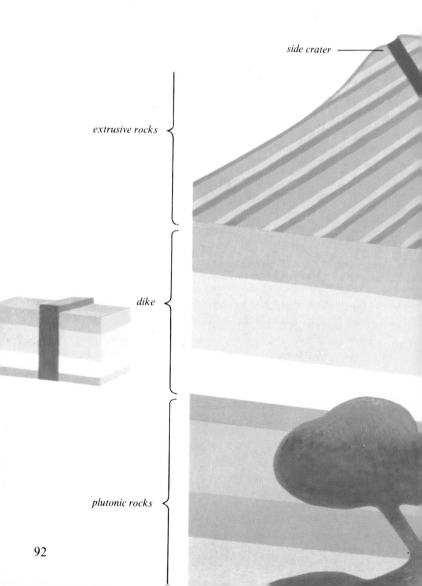

*Schematic section through a volcano.
Magma moves up through a crater from
the underground magma chamber. The
lava and loose 'explosion products' then
build up the volcano. When magma
solidifies in joints it forms veins or dikes;
if the veins follow the layering or bedding,
they are sills. Plutonic rocks are magma
which has solidified deep inside the
volcano*

volcanic crater ⸻

side crater ⸻

extrusive rocks {

dike {

plutonic rocks {

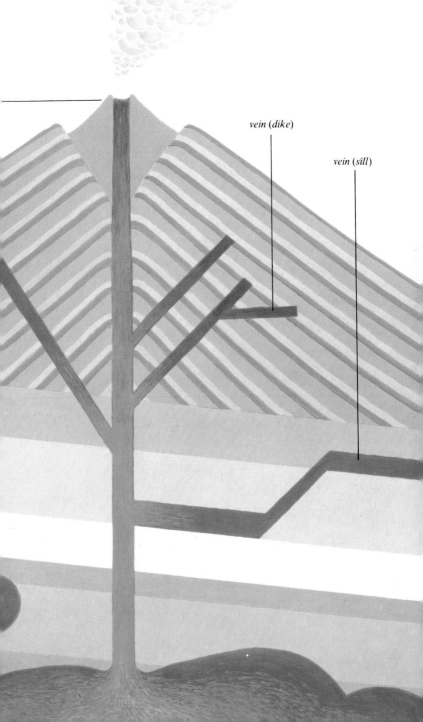

vein (dike)

vein (sill)

Of the three important magma types, basaltic, andesitic and granitic, the latter only rarely forms volcanoes. All, however, represent the partial melting of three different materials: gneiss, peridotite and ocean-floor crust plus sediment, and thus have different compositions. Granitic magma is rich in silica and relatively poor in iron and magnesium. In contrast, basaltic magma has little silica but is rich in iron and magnesium. Andesitic magma lies between the two, containing silica, iron and magnesium.

The magma composition determines which minerals will form when the magma solidifies. There is such a large silica content in granitic magma that the rock will always contain quartz. Basaltic and andesitic magmas have correspondingly small amounts of silica so that they solidify to rocks without a significant quantity of quartz. The elements iron and magnesium are important constituents of the dark minerals pyroxene, amphibole and biotite. Basaltic magma, which is rich in these elements, therefore solidifies to a dark rock with a high content of dark minerals, while andesitic and granitic magmas solidify to lighter rocks in which feldspar (and in granite, quartz) predominate.

The solidification process, which takes place in many ways, is of critical importance in the final appearance of the volcanic rock. If solidification was slow the rock will be coarse-grained because the individual crystals have had plenty of time to grow. The more rapid the solidification the more fine-grained the rock because there is scarcely any time for crystallization.

Crystallization of molten magma

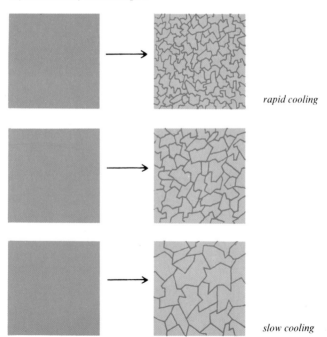

rapid cooling

slow cooling

94

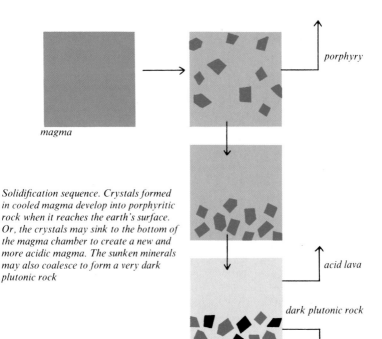

magma

porphyry

acid lava

dark plutonic rock

Solidification sequence. Crystals formed in cooled magma develop into porphyritic rock when it reaches the earth's surface. Or, the crystals may sink to the bottom of the magma chamber to create a new and more acidic magma. The sunken minerals may also coalesce to form a very dark plutonic rock

The speed of solidification or crystallization is decided by the rate of cooling which, in turn, depends on the way the magma solidifies. Some magma never reaches the surface but solidifies deep in the earth in 'magma chambers', or in fractures spreading out from a magma chamber. Deep down, cooling takes place so slowly that it can easily be thousands of years before all the magma in a large chamber is crystallized. This is how very coarse-grained rock occurs. Magma which reaches the surface and runs out as thin lava flows will, in contrast, cool quickly into fine-grained rocks, with the finest-grained occurring at the top and bottom layers of the flow where chilling is greatest. Magma which solidifies in cracks forms a 'medium-grained' rock, but it is not normally possible to determine from a loose pebble if the rock was formed in a crack or, for example, in the middle of a thin lava flow.

It often happens that crystallization begins when the magma is still deep in the earth, but finishes on the surface. Large crystals from deep down float around in the magma and are carried to the surface where there is rapid crystallization. The remaining magma solidifies to a fine-grained mass between these large 'phenocrysts'. A porphyritic texture results and the rock is a porphyry.

Coarse-grained rock from magma crystallized in a chamber deep in the earth is plutonic and forms a major igneous dome called a batholith. If crystallization takes place in cracks or fissures, which are termed 'dikes', the rock is hypabyssal, while extrusive rock comes from magma solidified on the surface. Also included with lavas, under the term extrusive, are rocks formed from volcanic ash and other 'loose eruptive products'.

Plutonics other than granite

We have described how plutonic rocks are crystallized at depth in a magma chamber with a later period of upheaval and erosion that finally 'unroofs' them at the surface. Basaltic magma crystallizes normally to the plutonic rock gabbro, but can simultaneously form other plutonic rocks such as peridotite. Andesitic magma crystallizes at depth to form diorite, but a variant which has less silica, iron and magnesium content can crystallize into, for instance, syenite.

This is a group of very dark rocks with a coarse- to medium-grained texture. The most important minerals are plagioclase, pyroxene and olivine, an olive-green mineral that looks like green glass splinters. One of the most common basic plutonic types is gabbro, formed chiefly by plagioclase and pyroxene. In a typical gabbro the flat, slender, box-like plagioclase grains are seen as small rectangles on the surface of a pebble. With the addition of olivine the rock becomes olivine gabbro.

There are almost no light-coloured minerals in peridotite and the rock pyroxenite. Peridotite is chiefly olivine and pyroxene, while pyroxenite is virtually only pyroxene. In all these rock types smaller amounts of metallic-looking ore minerals may be present in addition to the named minerals. Gabbro is sometimes a component of smaller intrusive bodies called lopoliths in instances where there are also layers of py-

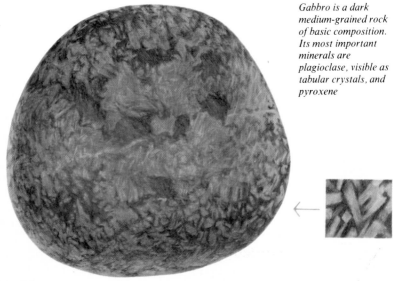

Gabbro is a dark medium-grained rock of basic composition. Its most important minerals are plagioclase, visible as tabular crystals, and pyroxene

roxenite and peridotite. In Britain, the famous Black Cuillins on the Scottish Isle of Skye are made of gabbro – contrasting in colour with the neighbouring granitic Red Hills.

Peridotite is an especially important rock type because it makes up the upper part of the earth's mantle. Normally one cannot see the mantle, but it can happen that lumps of peridotite are found in basalt lava; they are believed to be pieces of the mantle that broke loose and were carried to the surface in basaltic magma. During mountain building, pieces of the upper mantle can become mixed with the range's crustal rocks.

Peridotite is greenish and coarse-grained. In this example the nodules contained in the basalt are probably fragments of the earth's mantle

Larvikite is a coarse-grained syenitic rock with large, blue-tinged feldspar crystals

Pale, quartz-free, plutonic rocks

These pale, coarse-grained rocks are devoid of, or almost lacking, the mineral quartz. The main minerals are pale feldspars, while the dark minerals, such as biotite, amphibole and/or pyroxene, make up less than half the content. Diorite, with plagioclase as its most important feldspar, is the darkest of this group. There is often less than 20% of dark mineral in syenite because alkali feldspar is its dominating mineral. Larvikite is a special type of syenite in which feldspar crystals have a characteristic blue tinge (labradori-

zation). Alkali feldspar and the mineral nepheline are components of nepheline syenite, which can be light greyish, yellowish or reddish, with a slightly greasy appearance.

Diorite forms from the slow crystallization of andesitic magma. The more silica-poor magma types produce syenite and nepheline syenite in a similar way. Diorite and syenite are related to granite in mountain-root zones but they can also make smaller intrusions, especially of diorite, in association with andesitic lavas, as in parts of Snowdonia in northern Wales.

Syenite

Diorite

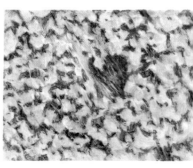

Extrusives

Extrusive rocks result when magma either flows over the earth's surface as rivers of lava, or when it forms volcanic ash. The magma's composition, especially its silica and gas content, determines whether lava or volcanic ash results. The amount of silica or silicic acid greatly influences the viscosity of the magma or lava. A silica-poor ('basic') magma such as basalt moves freely as fluid lava. A lava stream of basaltic magma can therefore flow a long distance before it solidifies, meaning that basaltic volcanoes are generally low and shield-shaped. Andesitic and, to a greater degree, granitic magmas have a larger silicic acid content ('acid' magma types) and are therefore more viscous. The volcanoes, then, are steep and conical since the lava travels only a short distance before it cools and solidifies.

The gases in magma, such as steam and carbon dioxide, are greatly compressed due to the high pressures in the depths of the earth. When a magma surfaces in a volcanic eruption, however, the reduced pressure allows these gases to expand, sometimes with great violence. Depending on the magma's gas content, the gas either bubbles in the glowing lava or makes a lava scum.

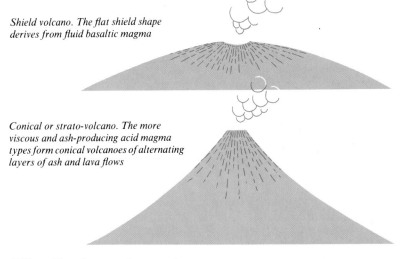

Shield volcano. The flat shield shape derives from fluid basaltic magma

Conical or strato-volcano. The more viscous and ash-producing acid magma types form conical volcanoes of alternating layers of ash and lava flows

Caldera. After a large eruption, so much lava may have flowed onto the surface that there is little material left in the underground magma chamber. The volcano may then collapse, leaving a deep, circular surface depression

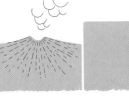

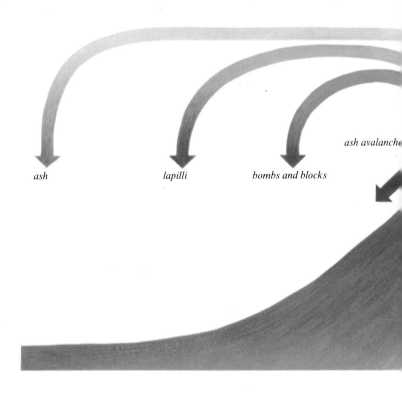

ash   lapilli   bombs and blocks   *ash avalanche*

But, if the gases expand violently, the lava explodes into millions of pieces of volcanic ash, especially if the lava is highly viscous.

Basic lava, of low viscosity, contains only modest amounts of gas, and thus there are rarely large amounts of ash from basic lava. The more acid lava types are, in contrast, often viscous and rich in gases and frequently cause explosive eruptions and the spewing out of great quantities of ash.

Basic extrusive rocks

Basic extrusive rocks are dark, often completely black, usually compact or fine-grained, but occasionally can have a phorphyritic texture. Their most important minerals are pyr-

oxene, plagioclase and ferrous ores. If the lava is of a porphyritic texture, plagioclase (as flat crystals) or olivine usually form the phenocrysts. Basalt is one of the commonest varieties of the fine-grained or compact basic lavas but its blackness is often hidden beneath its surface. It cools to form remarkable six-sided columns. The slightly coarser-grained basalts, found as dikes, are diabase or dolerite, while olivine basalt contains olivine which may occur as phenocrysts. Basalt is, as a rule, compact and without holes, although it may also be porous vesicular basalt. Lava with large pale or white 'amygdaloidal' vesicle fillings is not uncommon – a basaltic lava of this character is an amygdaloidal basalt (see p. 102).

100

The acid viscous magma types, particularly rich in gases, produce 'loose eruptive products'. The coarsest-grained are volcanic bombs and blocks, the intermediate grain-size deposits are lapilli and the finest-grained are ash. Volcanic ash also creates ash avalanches on volcano slopes

Amygdaloidal basalt pebble. Fine-grained basalt in which white minerals (zeolites) fill the amygdales (vesicles)

101

Basaltic rocks represent the rapid crystallization of basaltic magma on the earth's surface, or the in-filling of dikes when there are splits in the crustal rocks. The gas content of basaltic magma is minimal, but there is nevertheless enough to create lavas with varying numbers of vesicles. These form when the gases bubble out as the magma reaches the low pressure at the earth's surface. They are, therefore, a certain sign that the magma has been transformed into surface lava. After solidification, any percolating water fills in the vesicles with whitish minerals, making the lava amygdaloidal.

Basalt (kinnediabase). Coarse-grained basalt made up of large pyroxene and feldspar crystals which give the weathered surface a characteristic 'cauliflower' appearance

However, amygdaloidal rocks can result from all lava types – it depends on the actual volcanic processes more than on the rock type whether or not vesicles will form.

Basalt is one of the most common rock types. It builds shield volcanoes, makes up the ocean-floor crust, occurs on land as 'plateau' basalt, and often as basalt dikes. In plateau basalt, with eruption from long fissures, the fluid lava covers large areas. There are extensive basalt plateaux, formed about 50 million years ago, in Iceland, the Faroe Islands, western Scotland and Northern Ireland.

Vesicular lava is a compact pale rock with vesicles (bubbles) formed by gases in the magma which remain dissolved while it is still deep in the earth. The low pressure on the surface, however, causes them to separate rapidly, making bubbles in the still-liquid lava

Plateau basalt erupts from long volcanic fissures. The individual lava streams extrude onto the surface in thin layers, but successive flows from different fissures may overlap to form a single large basalt plateau

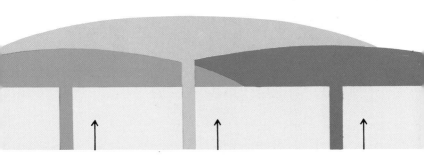

103

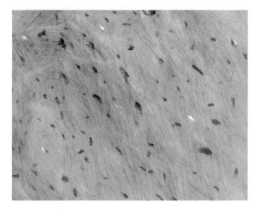

A pale variety of the lava andesite showing fine-grained groundmass with flow structure and dark amphibole and biotite phenocrysts

Intermediate and acid extrusive rocks

Most andesites are intermediate lavas which, with increasing amounts of quartz, pass into the acid lava dacite. They are very fine-grained with marked flow structures. Medium-grained rocks resembling andesites in mineral composition but containing phenocrysts are porphyries (rhomb-porphyry). Rectangular porphyry exhibits box-shaped feldspar phenocrysts on a pebble's surface. A porphyritic rock with quartz phenocrysts is a quartz porphyry. When free quartz exceeds 10% the lava is said to be acid.

In Britain, examples of intermediate andesites and acid rhyolites are commonly found in the Ordovician volcanics of northern Wales (Snowdon, Cader Idris) and the Lake District (Borrowdale). Porphyritic rocks can be seen in south-western Scotland and the Cheviot Hills. Rhyolites are the most acid of the extrusives and are so fine-grained or glassy that it is difficult to establish their true character without chemical analysis. Thus, compact

Rhomb-porphyry can be identified by its large rhomb-shaped feldspar grains which form phenocrysts in a medium-grained matrix

pale volcanic rocks, with or without small phenocrysts, which show 'flow lines' and 'spherulites' are collectively called acid lavas since the mineral content and hence the precise composition cannot easily be determined. Flow lines can resemble bedding but, as a rule, look more like sinuous drawings in the rock. Elongated amygdales and lines of phenocrysts can also indicate flow and may help to prove that the rock must therefore have been a lava. Spherulites, up to pea-size sphericle particles, are often a different colour from the rest of the rock and do not have compact grains. The more coarse-grained rocks may also contain spherulites, with the larger ones more or less merging into irregular layers.

Feldspar porphyry. Phenocrysts of feldspar are the thin, tabular or box-shaped grains in a dark, medium-grained groundmass. When the feldspar phenocrysts are large and rectangular they are rectangular porphyry

Pumice, a strongly vesicular compact lava, floats on water. When it is a pale colour it is derived from acid lava, but is from basic lava when darker. In earlier times pumice was used as sanding cork and in place of soap for washing the hands. The rock obsidian, a black glass without crystals, can contain spherulites. Its colour, glassy lustre and conchoidal fractures are all identifying characteristics.

Quartz porphyry is porphyritic with a compact, red-brown groundmass and phenocrysts of quartz and feldspar. Quartz-rich lavas are usually referred to as rhyolite

Spherulites in a lava are the glass droplets that, through delayed crystallization in the lava, have formed a compact material of a different colour

Tuff is a hardened volcanic ash, which can be dark if it comes from basic magma, or pale if from acid types. Tuffs are often layered: the grain size may vary, with the finest fragments at the top and the coarsest at the bottom. They can include larger lumps of lava which must have fallen into existing ash layers. Layered or bedded tuffs can sometimes be mistaken for sedimentary sandstone, but the sharp-edged individual grains may be minerals such as pyroxene, which are found only very rarely in sandstone. Coarser-grained rocks chiefly of solidified lava lumps (volcanic bombs) are called agglomerates. Tiny sherds of volcanic glass particles are identifying features of ignimbrite, a hard compact rock. Acid extrusive rocks are made up of andesitic, granitic and related magma types. If crystallization began while the magma was still underground the rock has a porphyritic texture in which there are coarser phenocrysts in a fine-grained or compact groundmass.

In porphyritic acid lavas the groundmass, or, in non-porphyritic rocks the entire rock, is often extremely fine-grained (compact). This is because the high viscosity of acid lavas makes it difficult for materials to circulate in the liquid and coalesce into large crystals.

When acid lava solidifies into a rock without identifiable grains the rock is pure glass, such as obsidian, or if possessing a quantity of small 'crystallites', a more compact example. Rocks transitional between these two can develop, consisting originally of glass, but becoming compact with time. Glass is usually thought of as an extremely viscous fluid which crystallizes extremely slowly – anywhere from several hundred to many thousands of years – but at higher temperatures the action is much more rapid.

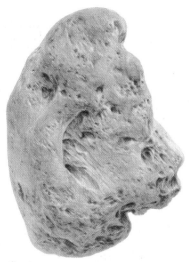

Pumice

A compact, red-brown rock which, because of its clear flow structure, can be identified as a lava

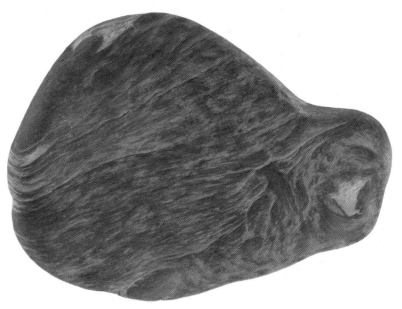

Obsidian, a volcanic glass, is recognized by its colour, lustre and conchoidal fracture

Tuff, of hardened volcanic ash, forms the dark, fine-grained layers at the top of the pebble. The lowest layers are sufficiently coarse-grained for individual ash particles to be visible and this is where small pyroxene crystals might be found

An acid lava often solidifies into a mixture of crystallite and glass 'beads'. Glass beads cannot be seen in an old rock because crystallization has already taken place and the beads have been converted into spherulites. The high gas content in acid magma types means that the eruptions of andesitic and rhyolitic volcanoes are very violent. These explosions create many small lava droplets which solidify in the air and become volcanic ash, which is then

deposited as tuff. Larger lava lumps (bombs) are also thrown out, together with big blocks of already solidified lava, for example from the crater rim. Deposits of bombs form the rock agglomerate if they accumulate in quantity.

Among the materials thrown out of a volcano there may be lava lumps with such a high gas content that the gas expands and forms a lava scum which solidifies in the air and showers down as pumice. Pumice can also come from the lava froth that flows from a volcano and is often found in, for example, the upper parts of an obsidian layer.

Under certain conditions the gases in a lava scum expand so forcibly that all the bubbles explode into clouds of glowing ash that roll down the side of the volcano like an avalanche, causing great destruction. Ignimbrite forms from the incandescent ash cloud when it cools as it comes to rest.

An agglomerate of broken pieces of a dark brown porphyritic lava in a dark grey tuff matrix

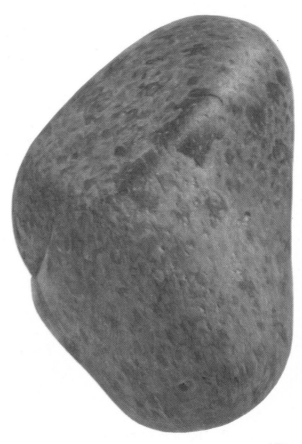

Ignimbrite. Different-sized sherds of glassy ash and pumice particles in a compact tuff matrix. The arrow indicates the direction and flow of the glowing ash avalanche which formed the ignimbrite as it cooled

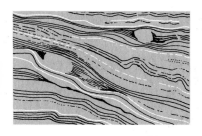

Flow structure. Many types of structures may be seen in acid lavas, which indicate that the rock was fluid. They can be irregular layers of differing grain size or colour, or layers with parallel-orientated phenocrysts

Andesitic extrusive rocks are associated with deep ocean trenches. The chemical composition of andesite is nearly the same as continental crust and it is probable, therefore, that all continental material originated in andesitic volcanes. Andesitic rocks have, through the passage of time, been subjected to weathering, transport, sedimentation, metamorphism, melting, upheaval and renewed weathering, which has made them the commonest igneous rock types of the continental crust. In addition, acid lava types can occur together with, for example, basalt. An eruption from a basalt volcano, which often starts with andesitic lava and ash, depends on how the magma crystallizes. In basaltic magma, crystallization can begin with olivine crystals. However, olivine contains more iron and magnesium and less silica than occurs in the magma itself. If, therefore, the olivine in the magma sinks to the bottom, the remaining magma will contain less iron and magnesium and more silica than the original. This 'residual magma' has thus become more andesitic. The andesitic type will lie uppermost in the magma chamber and is therefore the first out when there is an eruption. Granitic magma goes through the same process but results in lava of a granitic composition (rhyolite) being extruded early in the eruption in both basaltic and andesitic volcanoes.

In Le Puy, in southern France, a chapel perches on top of a 90 m high lava spine formed in the vent of a volcanic cone now totally eroded

Pebbles: their bands and patterns

Many pebbles have brilliantly coloured bands and patterns which make an otherwise dull-looking rock quite conspicuous. The banding can be due to normal layering, as in many sediments or in some igneous rocks such as tuff. In other instances the bands are due to minor igneous intrusions which, as veins, may cut through the pebble. There may also be unusual surface patterns.

Occasionally a pebble may be created from an actual rock junction, giving it two distinctive parts. One part may be basalt, pegmatite, granite or aplite with the other of a contrasting common rock. Some pebbles may consist of part of a dike, a basalt one, for example, and of its 'wall rock' into which the basalt magma was intruded, although this is a rare find.

A curious and very rare pebble formed at the junction of a basalt dike (dark) and a pink gneissic rock

Left: haematite veins along the edges of quartz veins in gneiss

Centre: epidote veins form thin pale green patterns on exposed bedrock

Below: quartz veins in fine-grained lava

Thin dikes are often called veins. If a vein consists of granitic material it is pegmatite, granite or aplite, according to grain size. Many veins can be filled with a single mineral, the commonest being the white quartzes and calcites, green or yellow-green epidotes and deep red haematites. A single pebble may be multi-veined – if they cross they were probably formed at different times, and if one vein cuts through another, it must be the younger of the two. Granitic dikes and veins are crystallized granitic magma in fractures in solid rock. Other types are usually deposits from solutions passing through the cracks. These 'migrating' solutions can also bleach or darken the surrounding rock. Thus one can find light or dark bands on either side of veins or cracks.

113

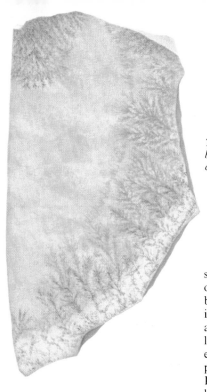

*Two types of dendrites on limestone :
brown iron and dark manganese
compounds*

If you split a mudstone or a limestone pebble, you can sometimes see,
on the broken surface, irregular
branching patterns. These dendrites,
iron or manganese compounds,
are often brown and look very much
like a pressed plant. They are
especially obvious when the deposition occurs in very thin cracks.
Dendrite-like deposits, which look
like irregular sunbursts in the rock,
can also develop away from the
cracks.

Stylolites

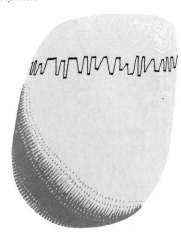

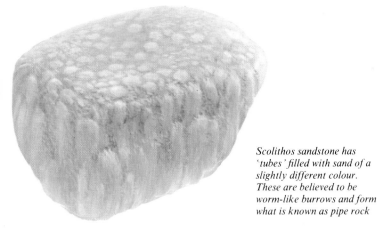

Scolithos sandstone has 'tubes' filled with sand of a slightly different colour. These are believed to be worm-like burrows and form what is known as pipe rock

Stylolites are particularly common in limestone as irregular, often pointed, dark-coloured 'seams'. Stylos means a column in Greek and, in a well-developed stylolite seam, the limestone does, in fact, resemble intertwined columns with the thickest, darkest layers at the top. Stylolites are actually formed from the solution and removal of a portion of the limestone. There is a varying content of mud and other insoluble particles in all limestones, which remains when the limestone is dissolved. The resulting dark seams mark the boundary in the rock where solution has taken place and left the darker material behind. Scolithos are sandstones with spotted tops and striped sides which look like a bundle of sticks. These vertical cylinders, or 'pipes', are thought to be the casts of worm burrows, and in Britain are found in Cambrian rocks near Inchnadamph in northwestern Scotland.

Footprints made by giant lizards from the Jurassic period

Geological time scale

Era	Period	Millions of years ago
Cenozoic	Quaternary	2
	Tertiary	65
Mesozoic	Cretaceous	136
	Jurassic	195
	Triassic	225
Palaeozoic	Permian	280
	Carboniferous	345
	Devonian	395
	Silurian	440
	Ordovician	500
	Cambrian	570
Proterozoic and Archaeozoic	Precambrian	600
	(oldest known rocks)	3,700

Subdivision of the Cenozoic, youngest era of the earth's history

Period	Stage	
Quaternary	Holocene	10,000 years ago
	Pleistocene	2 million
Tertiary	Pliocene	12 million
	Miocene	23 million
	Oligocene	35 million
	Eocene	55 million
	Palaeocene	65 million

Glossary of technical terms

acid test: a test for the calcite content of a mineral or rock. Drops of dilute (10%) hydrochloric acid are placed on the specimen; if bubbles form the test is positive

basic: rocks relatively poor in silica (silicic acid) but rich in magnesium and iron. The term is used only for the dark, mineral-rich igneous rocks

basin: an area where deposition takes place. The entire North Sea area is a large depositional basin

bedding plane: a surface parallel to the depositional surface in sedimentary rocks; a plane along which sedimentary rocks tend to split most easily

bitumen: often used for the various types of organic material (see below) in rocks – for example, asphalt, oil and coal – but it is important to note that not all coals are bituminous

breccia: a deposit of angular fragments implying minimal transport. The various types include cemented scree, fault (crush) breccia and volcanic breccia (agglomerate)

cleavage: a mineral's tendency to split along planes whose direction and importance are decided by its crystal structure

compact: in rocks, so fine-grained that individual grains can be seen only with a microscope. An example is mudstone (see table, p. 28)

continent: a major land area

continental drift: movement of the continents in relation to one another

core: the central (inner 3,471 km) part of the earth. It consists principally of iron and has a fluid outer part and a solid centre

crust: the earth's outermost layer, divided into continental crust, which is up to 30 km thick, and ocean-floor crust, about 10 km thick

crystal: a solid in which atoms or molecules are arranged in a precise and orderly pattern – the crystal structures – which therefore has a regular geometrical outer crystal shape. All minerals form crystals, but it is rare that the conditions of growth produce perfect ones

crystalline: a term generally used to distinguish the igneous and metamorphic rocks from the sedimentary rocks

current-bedding: a type of cross-bedding in sedimentary rocks, implying deposition by moving water. The bedding planes are inclined, thus indicating the direction of current flow

deep ocean trench: a chasm in the ocean floor in which the water can reach a depth of 10 km. The deepest known trench is the Marianas Trench in the Pacific Ocean. Others are the Japan, Java-Sunda and Peru-Chile

deformation: shape-changing. Most rocks are deformed plastically, i.e. like a piece of plasticine, when high temperature and pressure cause slow deformation. For example, folded layers develop deep in the earth's crust with this movement (see also *fault*)

delta: built-up sediments deposited in the calm waters of a river mouth

diagenesis: process in a sedimentary rock following deposition but which does not destroy the sedimentary features. For example, quartz precipitation in the pores of a sand deposit which converts it into sandstone, compression which changes clay to shale, or development of concretions

dike: a fissure filled with volcanic material, such as a basalt dike which cuts vertically across the bedding or rock layers. If the fissure runs parallel with the layers, however (following the boundary of a layer or bedding plane), and becomes filled with volcanic material, it is a sill

energy content: the violence of the means of transport in a depositional environment. If there is a large energy content the deposits will be coarse-grained; if it is small, the deposits will be fine-grained

erosion: removal of the earth's surface layer by the forces of nature. Erosion and weathering (see below) will break down mountains

extrusive rock: an igneous rock which solidified on the earth's surface. Examples are basalt, pumice and tuff

fault: a split, or break, along which movement takes place in the earth's crust. The two sides, separated by the split, move relative to each other

flow lines or *flow structure:* terms used to describe the mineralogical or textural banding of volcanic rocks (lavas) that were once fluid; also loosely used where micaceous layers are folded around larger crystals in metamorphic rocks

fossils: remains or impressions of ancient plants or animals preserved in sediments. A fossil usually consists of stony material. Fossilization can also be called petrifaction

glacial: formed by ice (glaciers) or in connection with glaciers

glass: a solid without a crystal structure

groundmass: the finer-grained material comprising the main body of a rock in which larger units (crystals, pebbles, etc.) occur

interior processes: processes in the earth's interior, such as metamorphism, magma formation and crustal movements

intrusion: magmatic (plutonic or dike) rock which is forced (intruded) into other rocks and then solidifies

lava: molten material on the earth's surface, which solidifies to a rock such as rhyolite

leading stone: erratic stone of a rock so characteristic that its place of origin can be identified

lithosphere: the outermost 100 km of the earth, made up of the crust and the upper part of the mantle. It is divided into large plates which move in relation to each other

loess: a deposit of mainly siliceous wind-blown dust which accumulates in ice-free areas adjacent to ice sheets. When re-worked by rivers, termed brickearth

magma: molten material in the earth's interior. A magma consists of a melt, mainly silicate material, together with various dissolved gases such as steam and carbon dioxide

magma chamber: magma-filled 'space' in the earth. When the magma crystallizes it forms an intrusion *mantle:* layer in the earth between the crust and the core

meander: winding pattern of a river channel through flat country

metamorphism: process in which rocks are changed through re-crystallization (see below) to new metamorphic rocks

mineral: a naturally-occurring crystalline chemical compound which can be identified with the help of its physical properties such as crystal shape, cleavage, hardness, streak, lustre, colour and density. These physical properties are decided by the mineral's composition and structure; mineral deposit is a term applied to a body (e.g. metal ore) of economic value (see *ore minerals*)

moraine or *till:* material deposited by ice or a landform made by glaciers

mountain ranges: the Alps and Himalayas are examples of mountain ranges

mountain roots: deep 'roots' of old mountain ranges which, by upheaval and erosion, have appeared at the earth's surface. In mountain-root zones, rocks such as gneiss, granite and crystalline schist are predominant. Shield areas are large areas of old mountain roots which form the continental interiors. Well-known examples are the Baltic Shield and the North American Shield of Greenland and Canada

ocean-floor crust: that part of the earth's crust which underlies the deep oceans. Formed at ocean ridges, it consists chiefly of basaltic material

ore minerals: chiefly sulphides and oxides of iron and other metals which, in contrast to the more widespread silicate minerals of common rocks, are not transparent when thin slivers are viewed under a microscope. Examples are pyrite and magnetite

organic material: a mixture of organic compounds, such as hydro-carbons, formed directly or indirectly from living organisms

pebble: a rock fragment with a diameter of between 4–64 mm

phenocrysts: large crystals enclosed in the fine-grained groundmass of igneous rocks

plutonic rock: magmatic rock (see above) slowly crystallized below the earth's surface ('at depth'). The most common one is granite

porous: with pores or holes, implying poor water retention

re-crystallization: formation of new crystals

regression: retreat (of water), as when coastal land surrounding the sea rises (or sea-level falls), and the shore line and coastal sea floor become land

rock: stone material. The earth's crust is built up of rocks which, in turn, consist of minerals. When a rock is made up of particular minerals and has a particular structure, it usually differs from other rocks. The rock quartzite, for instance, comprises the grains of only one mineral while the rock granite has grains of several

schistosity: a rock's tendency to split along particular planes

schlieren: short, more or less S-shaped veins

sedimentary rocks: rocks formed by deposition on the earth's surface. Sedimentary rocks may also result from true sedimentation (sandstone), precipitation (chemical sediments) and organisms (biogenic sediments)

sedimentation: process by which material is deposited

silicate mineral: mineral in which silicon (silica) is an important constituent. The most widespread rock-forming minerals (quartz, feldspar, mica, pyroxene, amphibole) are silicate minerals

structure: the pattern, which depends on how a rock's constituents are arranged. Layering and cross-bedding are examples of sedimentary structures; banding (in gneiss) and folding are structures in metamorphic rocks, and flow lines are structures in volcanic lavas

texture: a rock's surface pattern of grain boundaries

transgression: marine incursion, such as when an area is flooded by sinking land or rising sea-level. Transgression forms a series of strata in which coarser coastal deposits (basal conglomerate) are overlain by finer-grained sediments deposited in deeper water

veins: thin, often irregular, cracks filled with either magmatic material (pegmatites) or deposits from percolating solutions

weathering: the breaking down of surface rocks. Mechanical weathering, such as frost-shattering, differs from chemical weathering (rotting)

Further reading

Allen, J. R. L., *Physical Geology*, Allen & Unwin, 1975.

Hamilton, W. R., Woolley, A. R. and Bishop, A. C., *The Hamlyn Guide to Minerals, Rocks and Fossils*, Hamlyn, 1974.

Hatch, F. H., Wells, A. K. and Wells, M. K., *Petrology of the Igneous Rocks*, 13th edn, Thomas Murby & Co., 1972.

Holmes, A., *Principles of Physical Geology*, 3rd edn, Nelson, 1978 (in paperback).

Kirkaldy, J. F., *Minerals and Rocks in Colour*, 3rd edn, Blandford, 1976.

Owen, T. R., *The Geological Evolution of the British Isles*, Pergamon, 1976.

Pettijohn, E. J., *Sedimentary Rocks*, 3rd edn, Harper & Row, 1975.

Pough, F. H., *A Field Guide to Rocks and Minerals*, Houghton Mifflin, Boston, 1957.

Read, H. H., '*Rutley's Elements of Mineralogy*', 26th edn, Allen & Unwin, 1970.

Read, H. H. and Watson, J., *Beginning Geology*, Macmillan, 1966.

Trueman, A. E., *Geology and Scenery in England and Wales*, rev. edn by Whittow and Hardy, Penguin Books, 1977.

Tyrell, G. W., *The Principles of Petrology*, Science Paperback, Chapman and Hall, 1978.

Whitten, D. G. A. and Brooks, J. R. V., *A Dictionary of Geology*, Penguin Books, 1972.

Whittow, J. B., *Geology and Scenery in Ireland*, Penguin Books, 1975.

Whittow, J. B., *Geology and Scenery in Scotland*, Penguin Books, 1977.

Index

(Numbers in italics refer to pages with illustrations only)